Special Report 231

Transportation, Urban Form,

and the

Environment

Proceedings of a Conference

Beckman Center
Irvine, California
December 9–12, 1990

Sponsored by
Federal Highway Administration
Transportation Research Board

With cooperation and assistance of
U.S. Department of Transportation
Office of the Secretary
Urban Mass Transportation Administration

Transportation Research Board
National Research Council
Washington, D.C. 1991

Transportation Research Board Special Report 231

Subscriber Category
IA planning and administration

Transportation Research Board publications are available by ordering directly from TRB. They may also be obtained on a regular basis through organizational or individual affiliation with TRB; affiliates or library subscribers are eligible for substantial discounts. For further information, write to the Transportation Research Board, National Research Council, 2101 Constitution Avenue, N.W., Washington, D.C. 20418.

Printed in the United States of America

Library of Congress Cataloging-in-Publication Data

Transportation, urban form, and the environment: proceedings of a conference,
  Beckman Center, Irvine, California, December 9–12, 1990
  / sponsored by Federal Highway Administration [and] Transportation
  Research Board, with cooperation and assistance of Office of the
  Secretary, Urban Mass Transportation Administration, U. S. Department
  of Transportation.
        p.   cm. — (Special report ; 231)
    Papers of the Conference on Transportation, Urban Form, and the
  Environment.
    ISBN 0-309-05113-4
    1. Urban transportation—United States—Congresses. 2. Urban
  transportation—Environmental aspects—United States—Congresses.
  3. Land use, Urban—United States—Congresses. I. United States.
  Federal Highway Administration. II. National Research Council
  (U.S.). Transportation Research Board. III. Conference on
  Transportation, Urban Form, and the Environment (1990 : Irvine,
  Calif.) IV. Series: Special report (National Research Council
  (U.S.). Transportation Research Board) ; 231.
  HE308.T74 1991
  388.4'0973—dc20   91-31996
                                                              CIP

Cover design: Diane L. Ross

Steering Committee for Conference on Transportation, Urban Form, and the Environment

Preface

The form of land use development is affected by land availability, price, topography, and transportation access, and land use patterns in turn affect travel demand characteristics. In recent years suburban activity centers have developed at locations with superior highway access, and these centers have characteristics that are very different from central business districts in the core. The form of land use development is also affected by continuing changes in economic structure, demographics, and life-style.

If we are to develop solutions to the problem of urban congestion, it is important to gain a better understanding of the interaction between land use and transportation characteristics and between economic and demographic characteristics and land use. What are the public costs and benefits of alternative land use configurations? Can the present land use patterns be modified to produce a more efficient transportation system? What are the economic disbenefits resulting from an inadequate transportation system? What urban form or transportation strategies could best achieve such national objectives as clean air and energy conservation? What urban forms would be more efficient for a transit-oriented system and what forms would be more efficient for an automobile-oriented system? How can automobile travel demand be reduced?

Solutions to urban congestion must increase the person-carrying capacity of the existing transportation infrastructure, provide for efficient movement of goods and land access, and at the same time address the mobility needs of an aging population and conserve energy and economic resources. To develop practical and efficient solutions, we need to analyze

* The forces that drive urban development, potential impacts of rising energy costs, renewed efforts to ensure clean air, and new technologies on future development patterns;
* Future transportation needs of the various segments of the urban travel market, including work commuters, suburban travelers, and the elderly;

• Alternative methods to serve future travel needs;
• Innovative techniques to maximize the efficiency of travel to and from scattered centers in a multinuclear urban form;
• Policies on taxes, land development, and travel demand management and their systemwide impacts and economic resource costs; and
• Impacts of transportation improvements on economic development, the environment, and social objectives.

The status of current knowledge and gaps in knowledge with respect to the aforementioned issues must be identified in order to develop a research agenda that provides the transportation community with the tools needed to develop more efficient future transportation systems. The approach and elements of the research needed in these areas must be defined. In this conference, the intent was to develop a preliminary agenda of proposed future research. Nationally known experts in the field of transportation, land use, and demographic interaction were commissioned to provide insights into (a) how and why urban areas have become congested, (b) how urban areas may satisfy their mobility needs efficiently, and (c) what research must be undertaken to assist in analysis, development, and implementation of solutions.

The Federal Highway Administration (FHWA) requested the Transportation Research Board to conduct a Conference on Transportation, Urban Form, and the Environment as part of FHWA's approved High Priority National Program Area project "Ensuring the Efficiency of Future Urban Transportation Systems." The project's overall objective is the examination of options for maintaining future urban mobility. The purpose of this conference was to bring together experts to

• Review the status of our current knowledge with respect to recent historical trends in urban development and transportation and their interaction with economic and demographic forces;
• Discuss solutions and innovative institutional and technical approaches to provide for future urban mobility; and
• Identify research needs to aid in the analysis, development, and implementation of such solutions.

Resource papers were commissioned on the following topics:

Housing and Jobs: Deakin focused on the demand for transportation as determined by land use, demographics, and so forth. The primary focus was on issues involved in connecting origins with destinations. She included discussion of private development funding and public development-regulatory aspects.

Financing: Parker addressed the public costs attributable to urban form and public financing mechanisms that affect development and determine land use. He also included developer financing and joint development issues and economic impacts.

Decision Making: Porter examined how the structure of institutions influences urban form and local and regional decision making. He included the politics of urban form and the differences in the land use and transportation decision process.

Energy and Environment: Burwell examined the energy requirements of urban form (particularly transportation energy), the effects of development and land use on the environment, and regional economic opportunity costs associated with different patterns of land use.

Options: Brand discussed options for serving existing travel patterns, controlling demand, improving system performance, and restructuring the transportation network to better meet demand and telecommunications and telecommuting.

Urban Design: Dyett focused on site design and its relationship to urban form and transportation. He emphasized design strategies that reduce travel needs and requirements related to residential and job requirements. Although emphasis was on the micro level, regional implications were considered.

The keynote address, giving a decision maker's viewpoint of transportation, urban form, and the environment, is also contained in these proceedings. After the resource papers were presented, the participants formed five workshop groups to discuss the same topics covered by the authors (e.g., basic understanding, relationships, methodology). A final plenary session was held at which the workshop reports were presented, followed by open discussion.

This conference report represents the first step in a two-stage process of developing a research agenda. Findings from this conference will be expanded by the Transportation Systems Center, U.S. Department of Transportation, in order to develop a comprehensive research agenda on the topic of transportation, urban form, and the environment.

Contents

1
Introduction

Overview

ALAN E. PISARSKI
Consultant, Falls Church, Virginia

The attempt to express, much less understand, the nature of the relationships inherent in transportation, urban form, and the environment is a great challenge. Analysis can be overwhelmed by the inextricable linkages between them, each shaping, and shaped by, the others.

Moreover, the goals and purposes that drive human activity make up a fourth element in this set of relationships that is sometimes overlooked. For it is the human actions and values involved that are the ultimate shapers of transportation, urban form, and the environment. There is a tendency to become too mechanistic in these analyses: transportation drives land use change, land use forms transport demand, transportation changes environment, and so forth. It is the human dimension that forms and shapes all of these elements. Our sense of the interactions of these sectors will only be complete when they have been properly incorporated into the understanding of human needs, values, and purposes.

Understanding is also shaped by the professional goals and perspectives of the participants. Urban planners, perhaps because the public policy levers seem strongest there, see transportation as a tool for action to effect change in the form and structure of the urban environment, rather than as an end in itself. The focus of environmental professionals is on the consequences for the environment in all its aspects, from varying levels and kinds of transportation activity to varying categories of urban form and structure. The concern of transportation planners is the consequences for urban form and the environment of public policies and plans regarding transport. This concern has two elements: the first is the product of the fact that urban form and environment are valued as ends in themselves and therefore there is a desire to know of pending threats to them; the second concern, primarily in the area of urban form, is that changes wrought by transportation can feed back to the transportation equation and modify the context for the plans initiated and, at least partially, vitiate the intended benefits of the planned improvements. This final point helps make the case for the argument that the transportation planner must also be prepared to examine the effects of urban form and the environment on transportation.

In a literature synthesis provided for this conference, Giuliano identifies the intricacies and complexities of the past efforts to pin down the relationships that are the subject of the conference. It is clear from her work that no obvious and simple conclusions are forthcoming from past research with respect to what urban form is "best" or what transport system best promotes that best system of land use distributions. The answer, it appears, is that "it depends." And it depends on a lot of things—the definition of efficiency adopted, the costs of goods and services (notably transport and land costs), and the activity structure and preferences in the society and the economy at present and in the future.

It can be inferred from Giuliano's paper that an understanding of transportation and urban form, however defined, is derived through the interactions of accessibility and density—accessibility as the "real" product of transportation and density as the primary expression of urban form. The reader may benefit from this simplified approach to understanding this complex topic. In these terms, then, the challenge to this conference is to establish the research base to better understand the interplay among accessibility, density, and environment. Even identifying research needs for the topic redefined in this somewhat oversimplified way is a daunting challenge.

An overall structure was established to guide the discussions of the five workshops. This involved treating six topics:

1. Housing and jobs,
2. Financing,
3. Decision making,
4. Energy and environment,
5. Options, and
6. Urban design.

Each of these topics was the subject of a paper by a selected researcher as an introduction to the conference activities. (Their papers appear elsewhere as part of these proceedings.) These topics were addressed within the overall scope of four guiding themes:

1. Basic understanding and relationships,
2. Methodologies,

3. Policy and institutions, and
4. Research recommendations.

Conceptually these elements formed a matrix of 24 cells within which research topics could be discussed and a research agenda established. This matrix was not rigidly pursued in the development of the research agenda.

The participants in the five workshops carried on their work independently and selected their own individual approaches to the task at hand. They tended to choose different areas for emphasis, and consequently made varying levels of progress in different topic areas. Thus the overall findings and the structures used to organize those findings by each workshop, within the conference-specified rubric, varied from group to group. It is instructive about the nature of this topic that the structural treatment given the subject varied so substantially among the five workshops.

However different the approaches, there was a striking degree of agreement about the nature of the problems and the nature of future research needs among the five workshops. Within their varying structural contexts, the actual detailed findings of the workshops were relatively similar, although exhibiting different areas of emphasis. A large number of the research recommendations appeared in different form in all of the workshops.

The following synthesis of their findings and research recommendations is not intended to be exhaustive; rather it seeks to summarize some of the key findings and shared research themes developed by the five groups. It uses the three main guiding themes of the conference as a summarizing device, folding the fourth theme—research recommendations—into the three main elements.

BASIC UNDERSTANDING AND RELATIONSHIPS

Within the general theme area of basic understanding and relationships there was considerable agreement among the workshops that obtaining better data was the central concern. The data requirements were focused on both traditional and innovative data collection approaches designed to contribute to better understanding of some very fundamental relationships—relationships that many outside the transportation–land use fraternity would assume are fully understood by practitioners. Among the basic relationships whose understanding could supply better data were the following:

• **Underlying demographic and social changes and current activity patterns that are the basis for travel demand:** The relationship between household activity and travel demand is perceived only weakly. The social and economic values and preferences that modify these activities are also poorly understood. Traditional home interview surveys are required, but also needed are more sophisticated household surveys developed to reveal preferences and activity patterns. The intercity travel and tourism industry has pioneered in this area, but application to local travel behavior has been very limited.

• **Accessibility of transportation and the location decisions of private households and businesses.**

• **Current problems and potential solutions:** Transportation planning today attempts to incorporate a large and growing array of potential responses that may prove helpful in increasing capacity, reducing demand, or shifting travel to alternative places and times. This "toolbox" of available actions derives from the interest in substitutes for construction of new facilities or equipment. These prospective tools are untried and untested. Neither their effectiveness nor their unintended consequences are properly understood. The profession needs much more information about what works and what does not, and what the short- and long-term consequences of these actions might be. Cost-effectiveness data on prospective policy actions are needed to support options assessments. A compendium of success stories is proposed.

• **Congestion and the environment:** One of the central questions of the public policy debate is, What does reduction in congestion do for air quality? Is it positive or negative in the short term and long term? How much long-term growth would offset near-term pollution improvements from traffic congestion relief? What are the air quality measures to describe these relationships appropriately?

• **Transport-ameliorative actions and air quality:** The focus of interest was on having sufficient observation densities in metropolitan areas to permit assessment of changes, particularly improvements, resulting from transport-ameliorative actions. The air quality monitoring process must be sensitive enough to measure changes that come about from public policy actions in transportation and elsewhere.

Other areas that were not specifically data related were identified as needing greater understanding. Some of these were

• The effects of highway pricing and parking pricing on demand and urban form.

• The interaction between new technologies such as intelligent vehicle/highway systems and telecommuting on urban form and the environment.

- The description of density both for populations and other activities such as work. The data are available, but no effective descriptions have been prepared regarding the density levels at which Americans live and work, what the trends are in these densities, and what the likely future patterns of density are.
- The relationship between density and social and environmental objectives.
- The relationship between density and private- and public-sector costs and benefits.
- Trends in density preferences of business and individuals.
- The activities and effects on urban form and environment of urban goods movement.

METHODOLOGY

Methodological improvement was a significant component of interest for the five workshops. Some of the interests expressed overlapped with those identified as data needs and institutional interests. As a result, the allocation to the methodological area is relatively arbitrary. Some of the main points were the following:

- It was agreed that the entire subject area was seriously in need of a series of syntheses of current knowledge and practice, as has been so effectively developed by NCHRP. The benefits to the profession from such a series of small, low-cost studies would be very great. They would benefit public officials as well by expanding their understanding of the relationships involved. The synthesis prepared by Giuliano for FHWA was an excellent foundation for the work needed in this area.
- Each workshop raised the subject of models for simulation, analysis, and forecasting. Some held the view that new models need development; others took the view that current models are effective and useful but that data and funding to permit greater use of these tools are lacking. General agreement existed that modeling has a major role to play in this area and that the research effort has to be dedicated, well financed, and with a long-term view regarding payoffs.
- A number of workshops identified the document *The Cost of Sprawl* from the early 1970s as needing revision and updating. This revision was seen as a real opportunity to review the actual costs

and benefits of various density levels and urban development patterns.

• Several groups found that level-of-service measures as an expression of transportation effectiveness need revision to reflect broader accessibility characteristics than those expressed by highway capacity. For instance, high-occupancy vehicle and automobile alternatives need to be encompassed in an overall measure of access. Further in this direction, they called for a review of the Institute of Transportation Engineers manual in use for trip generation and travel estimating purposes.

• All groups placed heavy emphasis on the need for greater system performance measures. Again the emphasis was on multimodal capability to capture travel time and cost characteristics of transport mobility and accessibility.

• One group summarized much of the discussion by calling for "a system of accounts" for urban travel, air quality, and congestion. Such a system would bring together all of the main measures of cost and service in a uniform transferable format.

POLICY AND INSTITUTIONS

Discussion about policy and institutions was directed to a great extent at the effectiveness (or lack thereof) of metropolitan planning institutions, the public decision making process, and the new demands being made for better coordination of responsibilities for action among all levels of government. Among the themes identified were the following:

• The groups found a great need for the communication of "success stories" in which communities took effective action in handling travel demand and improving air quality and mobility.

• There was parallel concern for the pressures on communities to move quickly to deal with problems of long duration. In the "rush to action," as one group described it, there is not enough time to study new policy options that are pressed into action without knowledge of their consequences. The effectiveness of prospective public policies regarding job/housing balance is a case in point.

• Each of the workshops found the subject of financial resources to be a continuing concern, in particular the ability to aggregate funds from different sources to focus on a specific problem. Greater research was found to be necessary about the effects of various revenue measures enacted in the transportation sector outside of their direct revenue consequences.

• The groups identified as a concern the inability to judge the effectiveness and results of planning.

• The groups identified as a key concern the nature and effects of taxation systems and their effects on decision making. The impacts of the use of tolls, for example, are not fully understood. Other revenue devices have unexpected consequences that must be better anticipated.

• The groups found an area for considerable concern in existing processes of dissemination of research results, of knowledge, of what works, and of success stories. If more research is warranted, then greater effort in distributing the results of research is also warranted.

RESEARCH RECOMMENDATIONS

The groups prepared research recommendations in varying degrees of completeness: some produced lists of research projects; others added brief text; others produced almost full-scale work statements. Some of these recommendations were discussed earlier in this overview; all the research recommendations appear in the Workshop Reports section of these proceedings. This section concludes by briefly identifying and listing the eight main topical research recommendations. They are the following:

1. **Improved data:** Better data sets are needed to refine the detail of present transportation, land use, and air quality analytical capability [the Census Bureau's Topologically Integrated Geographic Encoding and Referencing (TIGER) system is a major resource]; to provide better understanding of the activity and motivational factors that underlie contemporary travel demand; to support the modeling and forecasting of land use and transportation; and to permit analysis of freight flows as well as the single focus on passenger travel.

2. **Options evaluation studies:** Evaluation and operational studies of the growing number of proposed new options for public action are needed. Public officials need to know what works—at what costs and with what consequences. Success stories and the associated knowledge that permits successes to be transferred between areas are necessary.

3. **Density studies:** Greater understanding of the transportation-density and environment-density relationship is called for. The development of syntheses, basic descriptive material, and documenta-

tion in this area is crucial for the profession and for public officials. Empirical studies of density and its effects are needed in the context of a new set of density descriptors.

4. **Assessment of urban form alternatives:** Overall evaluation of various alternative urban form constructs in terms of costs and benefits, public acceptance, and political and economic feasibility is a priority. Questions that must be answered include whether urban retrofitting of higher-density overlays on existing spread patterns is feasible and effective.

5. **System monitoring:** Systems performance monitoring capability is central to long-term effectiveness of transportation and environmental planning. Both transportation and air quality monitoring capabilities need improvement. Sensitivity to policy change in these systems is crucial.

6. **Improved research management:** Better research management (i.e., making better use of available research materials), broader dissemination, and more means to test and apply research results are critical.

7. **Enhanced tools of governance:** Government response mechanisms to meet the new challenges need careful review and research. New mechanisms for government, new planning approaches, and new means of coordination of complex activities requiring action across government levels and jurisdictions need research.

8. **More funding:** One overriding theme that came out of each of the workshops is better funding for the urban planning and urban planning research process. This sector has been starved in recent years with respect to funding for data, for research, and for analysis. With the new demands, options, and pressures placed on the process, the need for supporting funds and other resources has never been greater.

Keynote Address: Decision Makers Need Help

DAVID F. SCHULZ
County Executive, Milwaukee, Wisconsin

In the next 3 days, conference participants are being asked to give us decision makers some help—some help in providing transportation facilities and services that both respond to existing travel demand and serve people currently not served, some help in guiding the development of our urban areas to make them transportation-efficient and environmentally sound, and some help in operating and managing the existing transportation system to best effect. But first I want to share my vision of five realities of the urban transportation environment in the 1990s.

The first reality is that resources are scarce and getting scarcer. The past 10 years have been characterized by a decreasing willingness and ability on the part of the federal government to deal with domestic issues, including the provision of transportation. The overriding federal policy during this time has been to pass the buck to states, cities, and urban counties, not only for transportation but also for human services, health care, law enforcement, education, and the environment. Transportation in urban areas has been thrown into competition with other high-priority needs, with the inevitable result that the level of maintenance and development of the urban transportation system—highway and public transit—has declined. And given taxpayer revolt across the country, it is unlikely that the resource crunch will be alleviated any time soon.

The second reality is that the vast bulk of the transportation system that we will be operating in the year 2000 is already here. My subjective impression—which it would be interesting to confirm objectively—is that the total resources currently being devoted to the highway and public transit systems at the federal, state, regional, county, and municipal level are together insufficient even to maintain the existing systems in reasonable condition for the foreseeable future. The only way any current facilities or services are being expanded or new facilities or services developed is by in effect "stealing" money from the operation and maintenance of the existing systems. It should be clear where such a policy must inevitably lead in the long run.

The third reality is that people will continue to behave pretty much the way they do today. Although I intend to spend more of our time together here talking about this phenomenon, suffice it for the moment to say that I believe that those of us concerned with transportation in urban America can no longer wait for people to start to behave as we would like them to: living in compact, high-density residential development patterns; traveling short distances to work along well-defined corridors to destinations in orderly, compact business districts; using public transit in large numbers because they want to and not because they have to; planning their nonwork travel in orderly and efficient ways; and being very socially conscious in their selection and very limited personal use of an automobile. We have to recognize the reality that people are very unlikely to accept, and are in fact likely to strongly resist, significant changes of this sort, especially if they perceive that such changes are limiting their personal freedom of choice.

The fourth reality is that, despite the first three realities of very limited resources, a system largely already in place and by many accounts deteriorating, and the frustrating refusal of people to behave as our admittedly skewed transportation perspective requires, those same people do expect—nay, demand—that the transportation system in the 1990s deal with a number of vexing problems: the environmental damage it causes; the excessive energy it consumes; the time it wastes in traffic congestion; the deaths and injuries that some unsafe components of it cause, with their attendant human and financial cost; the urban sprawl it facilitates; and the poor job it does for too many of our people trying to participate fully in our economy and society. They also demand that the transportation system address all these problems while fulfilling its basic objective of supporting the underlying economic and social development of our cities, and do so without requiring that too much money be spent or that anyone's lives be disrupted for such foolishness as the taking of right-of-way for a new or expanded highway or transit line.

It should be clear that it is not likely that these problems are going to be successfully addressed totally, or even mostly, by maintaining the existing system of facilities and services, managing them better, and incrementally improving or expanding them. Therefore, the fifth and final reality is that, beyond maintenance, operational improvement, and incremental additions to current facilities and services, serious consideration is going to have to be given to what I would describe as significant changes in the urban transportation system: major new facilities and services, new or substantially modified technologies, and substantial changes in the way we use transportation and land. However, all of these changes, or others that are conceivable, share a common characteristic: they each face significant hurdles to successful implementation, most notably a great reluctance on behalf of the public, whose lot they would presumably improve, to accept them, let alone support and advocate them. And without public acceptance, support, and advocacy, these changes simply cannot be accomplished, however much they are needed.

However, as we consider how to make decisions regarding the provision of transportation and how we can do a better job of it, we can find a clue in this last reality. It is time for us to stop planning transportation for people and start planning transportation with people, start treating them like intelligent consumers of the services and facilities we provide, rather than mindless drones who won't do what we think is in their best interest.

Let me make a modest suggestion. A successful firm in the private sector, stuck with a product having the difficulties of our current urban transportation system, would resort to a process called marketing. Now, many people think that marketing is just advertising for some product or service. But advertising is only a relatively small part of marketing.

The three components of successful marketing are, first, market research; second, product design; and third, advertising and promotion. So let us spend the remainder of our time together using the marketing model to reflect about what the urban transportation agenda for the rest of this century should look like.

Let us start with market research. Typically, market research consists of systematically studying the marketplace in search of an opportunity to successfully produce and sell a product or service. From the perspective of the urban transportation system, clearly the product is the movement of people from one place to another. The urban travel demand modeling and forecasting process has been our primary version of market research.

However, most urban travel demand models are calibrated with data from comprehensive origin and destination surveys conducted in the 1950s or 1960s that have since been updated with infrequent surveys using small sample sizes. Well, the world of urban transportation has changed completely in the last quarter century. Suburbanization of both residences and jobs has exploded. Despite the best efforts of planners, in many areas development has occurred at densities far lower than can be served effectively by conventional public transit, so that the transit mode share has declined. Women have entered the work force in unprecedented numbers, and working single-parent heads-of-household have become relatively commonplace. Both these phenomena place significant new demands on the transportation system in terms of access to child care and the importance of travel time reliability. The loss in urban areas in the Northeast and Midwest of traditional manufacturing jobs overseas, together with nationwide economic changes emphasizing higher and better job skills, the growing plague of multigenerational welfare dependency, and the recent upsurge in legal and illegal non-English-speaking immigrants, have created ghettos of despair in virtually every central city in America. In these central cities, people are cut off by barriers of education, language, race, culture, economic change, and, yes, transportation from the sort of good-paying entry-level jobs that immigrants and poor people have historically used to fight their way up the ladder.

The important implication of these changes, at the market research phase, is that we must develop a renewed detailed quantitative understanding of the travel marketplace we are trying to serve. However, we must be careful not to view the market for travel as a monolith, but rather as an incredibly large series of market segments, each with its own transportation problems and opportunities. For example, the typical urban radial freeway and transit systems, adjusted for topography and geography and possibly complemented by a ring road or two, were designed to serve the work trips of the stereotypical central business district commuter. But downtown-oriented work trips have always been a minority of urban trips, and their importance has been steadily declining. In order to plan the transportation services and facilities of the next century, we need a detailed understanding of reverse commuting; suburb-to-suburb commuting; educational, recreational, and social travel; truck freight movement; and other aspects of this complex, segmented travel market.

This leads me to my first two fearless recommendations. First, we should resume regular detailed origin and destination studies in medium-sized and large cities. In addition to traditional trip data, these surveys should also include detailed data collection in the areas of travel and land use behavior. We really need to understand travel better at the household and individual levels to capture the complexity of travel behavior, because the choices of where, when, and how to travel are made at this micro level. Therefore, we need to supplement traditional areawide trip surveys with small precisely targeted sample surveys to measure travel attitudes and behavior within each of the multiple segments of the urban travel market.

Second, using existing data and the results of these new surveys, we should develop a detailed understanding of the highly segmented travel markets of urban areas, with special emphasis on identifying unserved and underserved market segments, particularly among people who are relatively powerless. Also, recognizing that people do not always behave as transportation planners may wish, this understanding should be firmly grounded in a consumer-oriented approach. This enhanced understanding of urban travel should be used in an effort to define the limits of public policy's ability to modify behavior in matters such as land use preferences, mode choice, automobile usage, and overall travel habits while identifying areas where travel behavior modification could possibly work and likely successful mechanisms and themes for such efforts.

Once market research provides an understanding of the market to be served in all its complexity, plans are developed for design of products to serve that market. Any successful product design must begin with an intimate understanding of present and past similar products in the marketplace. The urban transportation product design effort must therefore begin with a detailed appreciation of the existing transportation system, both physically and functionally. This is especially important given my second reality, that most of what we will have in 9 years is already here.

Therefore, my third recommendation is that we develop a comprehensive appreciation of the current condition of the highway and public transit systems in each urban area and the need to repair, replace, expand, or add to them. This appreciation should be augmented by nationwide efforts to look for generalizable patterns in the urban infrastructure. For example, exactly what constitutes the "life-cycle" of a facility needs to be better understood. Attention must be focused on the trade-off among initial investment, required repair and maintenance over the life of the facility, and the length of that lifetime itself. The out-year costs of both capital and operating decisions must be accurately and convincingly estimated, which would mark a major step toward achieving an appropriate level of infrastructure investment and reinvestment. This will not only allow development of better design standards, which I will discuss later, but will also allow the improved design and justification of managed maintenance and repair programs.

The advent of readily affordable, large-scale data management capabilities, especially in the area of storing mapped information, together with the ongoing development of computer-assisted infrastructure management capabilities, have the potential to provide accurate real-time information on the condition of the infrastructure systems in the field and allow priority targeting of scarce resources. My fourth recommendation is that we develop such capabilities in every large and medium-sized city in the country and look for common opportunities and problems in the development of such systems with an eye toward advancing the state of the art nationally in areawide comprehensive infrastructure data management.

By the way, don't you think it is about time that the dirty, everyday job of managing the infrastructure to achieve maximum performance is elevated in both importance and respectability? Oftentimes the most creative and imaginative—but least visible—people connected with the transportation system are those charged with facility operation. Agencies responsible for running a highway or transit system, or both, must give a high priority to managing that system in a manner consistent with the maximum possible productivity. The key is to remember that once operating improvements are implemented, they quickly fade away unless carefully and continuously cultivated. System management is an everyday responsibility. Therefore, my fifth recommendation is that we give the kind of respect and resources to the critically important job of managing our existing systems that the job deserves, including the recognition and support of outstanding system managers, research to advance the state of the art of highway and transit system management, and the transfer of significant advancements in systems management techniques and technology nationwide.

In light of the reality of limited resource availability, it is more important than ever that we ensure that we are getting the most for our money. There have been and continue to be problems with unrealistically high design standards for urban transportation facilities, which force a less than optimal use of resources at a time when resources are desperately short throughout the urban transportation system. Therefore, my sixth recommendation is that we accelerate the push for more realistic urban highway and transit design standards.

Those who advocate clinging to historically high design standards point with considerable justification to components of systems and sometimes whole systems that have served significantly greater demands than those for which they were designed, often without appropriate maintenance and sometimes without any maintenance at all, simply because they were overdesigned. Others point out, with equal conviction and credibility, that unrealistically high design standards, especially in urban areas, can drain scarce resources from other components of the system, leading to a situation in which parts of the system are overbuilt, whereas others have serious capacity and condition problems. I am not suggesting a solution to this dilemma, merely reminding you that it exists.

These revised design standards should also incorporate, to a degree not heretofore seen, provisions for future major reconstruction or replacement of the facility in question. For example, design standards must take into account how the deck of an elevated freeway can be replaced multiple times as it wears out while the supporting structure continues to function well. Similarly, the impact on service areas of prolonged outages for repair or replacement and how the effects of these outages can be minimized through shrewd farsighted design must be carefully considered.

Although they could conceivably be addressed under design standards, considerations of the environment, energy, and safety are worthy of a recommendation of their own. My seventh recommendation is that we develop project planning and design protocols with an underlying sensitivity to the environment, energy, and safety. This will not be limited to the perfunctory performance of an environmental impact assessment, but rather will spring from a real appreciation of the value and scarcity of the air, water, land, flora, fauna, and energy, coupled with the importance of transportation system safety. Our aim would be to develop projects to accomplish societal goals such as mobility and economic development in ways that minimize the negative impact on the environment, undue energy consumption, and unsafe transport conditions, and take reasonable steps to mitigate unavoidable harm. This development could be aided by a series of demonstration projects, which would experiment with alternative approaches to meeting this admittedly difficult goal.

The third phase of the marketing model is advertising and promotion. Clearly, we have not enjoyed the success for which we might have wished in changing people's behavior regarding transportation and land use decisions. Assuming that we can get some good data about likely targets of opportunity as I previously discussed, my eighth recommendation is that we identify the barriers to improving public acceptance of such desirable urban travel behaviors as riding public transit, ridesharing, creative work scheduling, efficient land development patterns, and others, as well as identify, on the basis of the experience of the last three decades of urban transportation planning and development, realistic limits on our ability to markedly change public behavior with regard to transportation and land use.

Once the barriers have been discovered, a realistically achievable advertising and promotion program aimed at encouraging appropriate travel behavior changes should be designed and implemented. However, at the risk of repeating myself, let me caution that we need to cut loose from our previous self-delusion that because something seems transparently obvious to the enlightened—us—it will automatically be slavishly accepted by "them." It is important that we not blame the customer for the problems of the urban transportation system and that we focus our efforts to change the way the customers use our services and facilities (and underlying all this how they use the land and how they develop our cities) on measures that are likely to be accepted, and accepted somewhat enthusiastically. If we as a society are unwilling and unable—and I believe we are—to directly control the use of land other than through the crude and imperfect tools of zoning and development guidelines, and if we are unwilling and unable—and I believe we are—to regulate people's travel other than through the crude and imperfect tools of parking supply and price limitations, public transit subsidies, and automobile fuel efficiency requirements, then we must focus our attention on land use and transportation behavior change measures that people want to accept.

As an aside, special attention needs to be paid to those relatively few people who may be asked to pay an inordinate share of the price of system improvement—those affected by property taking, unavoidable noise, and other direct impacts. Although mitigation measures need to be employed, there is a need to communicate the need at some point for appropriately mitigated sacrifice.

Because so much of the challenge we face is caused by current resource constraints, the advertising and promotion phase of our marketing effort needs to address public support for investment in the urban transportation system. For too long, transportation "needs lists" have been impossibly large, to the point at which elected decision makers and the general public are simply numbed. If we are to be successful in attracting public support for additional resources for the urban transportation system, it will be because we have made a convincing case of the real need for those resources. Therefore, my ninth recommendation is that we identify realistic urban transportation facility and service needs. Such a needs identification should start with an identification simply of what will be required to operate and maintain the existing urban highway and transit systems in decent order. Incremental programs for improvement can then be added. The direct relationship between infrastructure reinvestment and domestic productivity documented by a number of researchers provides the tangible evidence of both the need and the justification for additional infrastructure investment and should be further substantiated in the development of the new needs list I am suggesting.

It is probably also past time that we confront the reality that there may never be sufficient resources available to accomplish all that "needs" to be done. Although revised design standards will help, the bottom line is that we may need to scale back our previous ideas of what transportation services and facilities we can and should provide. We can begin by seriously questioning the unspoken planning assumption that we are going to maintain and operate all existing urban transportation services and facilities indefinitely. In point of fact, in the real world, we both add to and subtract from the system all the time as demands change. So we should probably also add a "don't needs" list, too.

In concluding my discussion of this marketing model, let me talk about the transportation planning and programming process. In an era of very limited resources, with urban transportation expected to solve a variety of challenges, planning has become, and must continue to become, more important than ever—not only regional system planning, but also planning at the community, corridor, and project levels, and, perhaps most important, land use planning. Planning represents the systematic quantitative anticipation of facility needs and provides for the provision of those needs in a way that minimizes overall cost—both capital and operating—and other negative impacts while maximizing benefit. Planning must be sensitive to both financial constraints and environmental imperatives. Plans that are unrealistic are worse than no plans at all, because a plan that cannot be implemented offers unattainable hope that a real problem can be solved with an unreal solution.

Planning must effectively confront that most difficult of obstacles: uncertainty. To do so, planners must find and admit where uncertainty exists, and leave sufficient flexibility to respond to a reasonable range of likely future circumstances. Planners must not prematurely foreclose alternatives or zero in on a single solution before critical forecast parameters subject to uncertainty can be verified by experience.

Programming can be an important tool, but only if it too is realistic. For too long, programming has been "wish listing," "trial ballooning," or both. Although they are valid exercises, they do not belong in transportation improvements programming. Programming must be realistically resource-constrained. This will force programmers to confront and resolve resource limitations and provide important feedback to the planning process on plan implementability.

Programming will also be tied as closely as possible to real decision makers—like me—for without our active involvement and concurrence, programming becomes a dangerous exercise in self-delusion. Therefore my 10th recommendation is that we recognize the increasing importance of the planning process; that we support the planning process with the time, energy, and resources necessary for it to work well; and that we continue to advance the state of the art of planning and programming techniques.

My 11th recommendation builds on my 10th. In many cities in the United States we are entering our fourth decade of comprehensive areawide coordinated land use and transportation planning. Although we have met with considerable success—notably in the provision of the basic framework of urban freeways, the development of other arterial streets and highways, and, in some cities, the start-up of new transit systems—we have also met with some failures—notably the apparent inability in many areas to control low-density resource-wasteful urban sprawl. Therefore, my final recommendation is that we comprehensively review our regional land use and transportation planning experience nationwide with an eye toward systematically identifying our successes and our failures, finding out, if we can, why some things worked and some things didn't, and use what we learn to recast the process to carry us into the next century. Again, however, we should do so with a keen appreciation of what is realistically achievable.

Urban America at the end of the 20th century faces a transportation challenge at least as great as that faced and overcome by the great railroad builders of the 19th century, the great urban transit system builders of the early 20th century, and the great urban freeway builders of the mid-20th century. Urban transportation infrastructure is wearing out, and requires maintenance, replacement, and—where appropriate—expansion. Continued urban development requires new transportation facilities and services. Concerns for the environment and energy must be addressed. Traffic congestion and transport safety are problematic in many areas. Many of the poor, the old, the young, and the disabled, together with working mothers and single parents, are ill served by the existing system. Tasked to solve these problems, the realities are that, first, resources are scarce; second, most of the system of the year 2000 is here today; third, people's behavior is unlikely to change to the degree some might wish; fourth, the list of challenges we're asked to face is daunting; and fifth, some big changes are going to be necessary if we are going to meet those challenges successfully.

I suggest a new approach to thinking about our urban transportation challenge. This new approach is modeled on the private-sector marketing approach, consisting of market research, product design, and advertising and promotion. On the basis of this new approach, I recommend 11 areas for those of us interested in the development of urban transportation to pursue:

1. Obtaining more and better travel behavior data;
2. Developing a better understanding of urban travel—a highly segmented market of great complexity;
3. Preparing and maintaining an upgraded inventory of the existing system—especially a detailed appreciation of the remaining "life-cycle" of major system components;
4. Enhancing the management and use of facility condition data;
5. Improving the management of urban transportation systems coupled with upgrading the transfer of systems management knowledge and technology;
6. Revising design standards targeted to fiscal realities and keyed to periodic renovation;
7. Increasing sensitivity of the design and planning processes to environmental, energy, and safety concerns;
8. Refining our understanding of public acceptance of travel and land use behavior changes, tied to increased efforts to promote realistically achievable changes in such behavior;
9. Updating and making more realistic our identification of urban transportation facility and service needs;
10. Supporting improved transportation planning and programming that deals better with uncertainty, is more realistic, and is more closely tied to decision makers; and
11. Reviewing the national experience to date with regional land use and transportation planning to identify success and failures.

This is the new era of urban transportation development. It is unlike any era that has gone before. It is more complicated, more difficult, more time-consuming, more frustrating, more technically demanding, and simply more challenging than its predecessors. It will require more time, patience, energy, understanding, and skill—

both technical skill and people skill—than any era of urban transportation development that preceded it.

If we are to successfully confront this challenging era, we must work together: federal, state, local government, academia, and the private sector. Frontline decision makers and technical practitioners must be buttressed by sound planning and far-sighted research and development. I believe we can successfully confront this challenge and that this conference represents a key step in successfully forging such a cooperative partnership and reasonable consensus on future directions.

2
Resource Papers

Jobs, Housing, and Transportation: Theory and Evidence on Interactions Between Land Use and Transportation

ELIZABETH A. DEAKIN
Department of City and Regional Planning and Department
of Civil Engineering, University of California, Berkeley

Relationships among jobs, housing, and transportation are much in the news recently. Suburbanization of employment is seen as straining the limited transportation facilities and services available there. Lack of affordable housing in reasonable proximity to employment centers is claimed to be causing lengthening commutes, at least for moderate-income households. Yet proposals to invest in new highways are challenged on the grounds that they might only serve to fuel another round of suburbanization and inner-city abandonment. Each argument has its counterarguments, fueling debate and contention.

Jobs, housing, and transportation interrelationships increasingly are on the minds of transportation researchers and practitioners, as well. This is a departure from earlier stances: for many years most transportation agencies took the position that transportation was put in place to serve development, and agency officials liked to say that they were not in the land use business. Although the point always could have been argued on effect if not on intent, today it is increasingly challenged from both perspectives. Transportation investments are sought to revitalize the central city, spur rural development, support economic growth and competitiveness, reduce environmental degradation, and improve social equity. If transportation agencies have

25

not been in the land use business, today many would argue that they should be.

Transportation investments are seen by many as instruments for the shaping of metropolitan structure and, indeed, for the transformation of metropolitan living. Rail transit proponents hope that major capital investments in a new round of rail projects will redirect urban growth patterns toward more compact, centered development. Proponents of new highways argue that economic development will be supported by the investments. Advocates of advanced highway technologies tend to focus more on congestion relief and safety benefits, but if the hoped-for order-of-magnitude increases in speeds and capacities are indeed attained, local, regional, and interregional land use impacts could be massive.

Although some seek to structure land use through strategic transportation investments, others seek to use land use planning techniques such as urban limit lines and urban density requirements to restructure the urban area and reduce or redirect the demand for transportation. At the smaller scale of urban design, a better matching of transportation to the specific land uses it serves is advocated. Design objectives aim for transit-oriented and pedestrian-friendly environments, with closer attention to street layouts and street widths, to sidewalks and bike facilities, and to planning for a balance of housing, jobs, and services.

Hopes that wise transportation investments and coordinated transportation–land use planning could improve the quality of life are matched by fears that transportation also could cause great, possibly irreparable, harm. Transportation's role as a major source of air pollution is a case in point: an emerging question is, Will transportation investments alleviate pollution problems by reducing congestion and smoothing out flows, or will they ultimately lead to higher emissions by stimulating land uses and changes in travel behavior that would offset any gains? That investments and policies will cater to the desires of the affluent and leave the urban less-advantaged behind is also a grave concern for many.

How, and to what extent, can transportation be expected to shape locational choices and support improved opportunities for jobs, housing, and other goods and services? To what extent can better coordination of transportation and land use improve overall performance? Can transportation's social and environmental impacts be tamed and redirected without recourse to its land use impacts? Theory and empirical evidence provide some insights but also raise a number of additional questions deserving of research.

This paper provides a brief review of the issues. It begins with a discussion of transportation–land use theory, focusing on residential and business location choice. It then summarizes key findings of empirical studies on the land use and urban development impacts of transit and highways. Land use planning approaches intended to moderate and redirect transportation demand are then discussed, along with urban design approaches. The paper concludes with a discussion of methodological concerns and research needs.

BASIC RELATIONSHIPS

Land use–transportation interactions have been the subject of a long tradition of inquiry, and a strong framework for the understanding of key relationships has emerged. Economic theories of location and land use are dominant, but sociological and historical theories also offer insights.

Location Theory

More than a century and a half ago, von Thünen (*1*) and Ricardo (*2*) observed that land, labor, and capital are the primary inputs of production and that the use of land is determined, in part, by its location. The location of transportation facilities and transportation technology determines the relative location, or accessibility, of places. Thus, land values as well as land uses reflect the relative locational advantages transportation systems confer.

Von Thünen (*1*) and Dunn (*3*), among others, dealt with agricultural land uses; Isard (*4*), Wingo (*5*), and Alonso (*6*), among others, dealt with the urban case. Kain (*7*), Mills (*8*), Anas (*9*), and others have extended and elaborated on the basic approaches. All of this group of models are rooted in land economics and in the concepts of optimality and equilibrium in land allocation.

In simple form, consider a center at which production and distribution activities are concentrated. Transportation costs increase with distance from the center, and in determining the amount to bid for land at a particular location, the bidder takes the transportation costs into account. All else being equal, location at the center minimizes transportation costs; land values therefore are highest at the center, and other locations will command lower rents reflective of their greater costs of transport.

But not all land uses would gain equally from a central location. If transportation is ubiquitous, a central location maximizes access to suppliers and to markets. Specialization is best supported by such a location, which also offers greater opportunities for economies of agglomeration and economies of scale than do less centrally situated sites. Activities that are specialized, that can capture the economies that central places make possible, or that need regular face-to-face contact with other firms, can minimize their costs by locating close together in central locations. They thus outbid others for space there.

Ancillary firms that provide goods and services to these central offices also need good access to the center but require less face-to-face contact (and probably have a lower-salaried work force, with lower values of time). Hence they will locate near, but not at the center. Other activities with less frequent need for central access bid less and locate further out. Housing is one such activity, because access to the center is primarily needed for employment. A balance is reached with particular uses characteristically found in central places, others in successive rings farther out.

The theory postulates a clear causality: Accessibility determines the worth of land for different uses at different locations. If transportation costs are changed, the rent gradients change; because land uses and rents for land are tied to each other by market processes, land use potentials are changed.

Applying this theory, investments that lower the cost of transportation to an employment center should simultaneously reduce the value of land at the center and increase the value at the periphery. Reduced commuting costs (or times, because time has value) would make it possible for commuters to spend more on housing, to travel farther, or both. If, as is usually the case, transportation is cheap relative to housing and one can buy more house per dollar farther from the center, households will have an incentive to live farther away from their work places. All else being equal, then, investments in transportation are likely to decrease residential density and increase the size of the urbanized area.

Applying similar reasoning, an increase in real income also would have a decentralizing effect. Population growth, on the other hand, would tend both to increase density in the center (because of greater competition for a fixed amount of land) and cause outward growth, as demand spilled over.

Business Location Theory

Business location theory, although developed along somewhat different paths, also rests on concepts of economic evaluation of transportation and other costs. Although some businesses are tied to particular sites because of needs for special qualities only available there, others can choose where to locate within an urban area by considering the relative costs and benefits of doing business at a particular place. Transportation is one such cost; businesses need access to goods and markets, and their labor costs reflect commuting costs. If transportation costs are reduced at a particular place, businesses there will be more profitable and better able to expand; other businesses also will find the location comparatively advantageous and seek to locate there. Thus, in theory, businesses will tend to congregate at points where transportation costs are low.

Population-serving businesses, which sell frequently purchased goods and services, are a special case, because their competitive edge depends in large part on their convenience to residences. If residences decentralize, these businesses follow, decentralizing this portion of the work force as well. The specific location of these businesses, however, still depends on the relative costs of transportation to alternative locations. A general reduction in shopping trip costs would permit population-serving firms to locate farther from residences and still be convenient to customers. Put another way, firms could attract customers from a wider area and still benefit from lower transport costs for inputs. In so doing, they might be able to lower costs, expand offerings, or both, and perhaps capture economies of scale and out-compete firms in less advantageous locations.

Overall, business location theory says that transportation improvements will tend, simultaneously, to increase employment at benefited sites and to decentralize workers' housing. Conversely, worsening transportation services will favor decentralization of jobs but support higher densities of housing.

Other Theories of Urban Growth

The bid-rent formulation of location theory focuses on economic factors in explaining the spatial distribution of various land uses. Alternative theories put forward by Burgess (*10*), Hurd (*11*), Hoyt (*12*), and others place greater emphasis on historical and social factors and cycles of growth and decline. Industries once located near the waterfront to use water transport and the water itself; their activities attracted workingmen's housing but repelled many other uses. The wealthier classes originally built houses near the center of the city, but as those houses grew obsolete, chose to build new ones in outlying areas made accessible by new transportation systems. Their

old houses filtered down to less affluent classes. Durability of buildings and infrastructure, along with patterns of blocks and ownership
of parcels, retarded change in land uses by making land assembly,
consolidation, and clearance difficult and expensive. Economies of
scale in building made new construction cheaper on vacant land, and
this further spurred suburbanization, quite apart from land rents.

Harris and Ullman's (13) work identified still additional factors
affecting development, including the need for specialized facilities
and services (transportation and other), agglomerations that support
mutual profitability, forced clustering of nuisances, and constraints
working against alternative housing location choices (lack of money,
class segregation). In this conception of urban growth, different activities would locate in distinct nuclei, or subcenters, because of the
interplay of these factors. Transportation would exert a different influence over location in the various nuclei because of different, specialized
needs of the occupants. Berry's (14) work has emphasized specialization of places and the growth of hierarchies of places, with both
historical factors and agglomeration economies playing a role.

Limitations of Available Theories

Both location theories and alternative theories on land use–transportation interactions provide useful insights but are limited by restrictive
assumptions and partial specifications of causal factors. Historical-
sociological theories have been largely descriptive, with few attempts
to extend them to formal prediction. Economic approaches, in contrast, have attempted to support forecasting; however, critics point to
the limited number of factors explicitly considered and note the restrictive assumptions on which the basic analytic models are based,
particularly in their highly abstracted mathematical forms.

Monocentricity of employment is perhaps the most widely criticized assumption, but other assumptions, including treatment of households as having only one worker, simplified treatments of topological
and temporal variations, and the assumed dominance of market forces
(that is, the exclusion of legal, institutional, and social constraints),
also are recognized limitations of this class of models. Several authors present detailed reviews and critiques, including Alcaly (15)
and Giuliano (16).

These limitations complicate and condition the lessons of the simple
bid-rent model of location and land use but hardly invalidate them.
As extended by researchers in the 1960s, 1970s, and 1980s, the theory
itself is broad enough to encompass multiple centers; indeed, such

centers would be expected to form as population moves outward, certain businesses follow markets, and others seek a supply of labor or cheap land on which to spread out. Agglomeration economies and specialization of places in a hierarchy or system of cities help explain the number of subcenters, whereas their location would perhaps be predictable as a function of relative accessibility, land availability, and other factors. The problem with these models is perhaps less a conceptual one than that mathematical tractability declines with each additional dose of reality.

Recent Models of Location and Transport Choice Processes

Adding realistic detail such as urban and suburban subcenters and multiworker households, and accounting for other important factors such as land availability, building quality, and the effects of social class, race, and local government services, requires simulation rather than analytic models. The results of such efforts generally support the relationships of transportation investments to land use and urban form postulated by location theory but also show that many other variables, including cost and suitability of land and buildings, labor market conditions, available services, social factors, and, for households, life-style and life-cycle considerations, are also critical factors in location choice.

Models developed by Lowry (*17*), Putman (*18*), Ducca and Putman (*19*), Herbert and Stevens (*20*), Prastacos (*21*), and others represent attempts to develop practical analysis and forecasting techniques for use in urban land use and transportation planning [see Hamburg et al. (*22*), Berechman and Small (*23*), and Bajpai (*24*) for reviews of the state of practice]. In general terms, these models allocate jobs and housing within a region as functions of accessibility, land availability, population and employment by category, income (for households), and other factors. Such models, although complicated and expensive, typically make several simplifying assumptions not wholly in accord with theory. At the same time, they typically overcome some of the limitations of pure analytical approaches; for example, travel times and costs can vary in different parts of the region and other spatial and socioeconomic heterogeneities can be entered into the assessment. Although in many applications this class of models has only moderate predictive capability, model applications nevertheless indicate the importance of transportation level of service to location decisions.

Other model developers have attempted to develop a stronger behavioral justification for location decisions. Prime examples are logit models of households' location and transportation choices [e.g., Lerman (25), Anas (9), among others]. These models typically include, in addition to land use and transportation accessibility variables, detailed household socioeconomic and life-style descriptors (including the number of workers present, household income, age of household members, presence of children, etc.). The studies confirm that transportation time and expense variables do matter—decisions on the location of jobs and housing do reflect concerns about transport costs. Other things being equal, congestion is associated with a preference for housing closer to work; long commutes are supported by better transport facilities.

For the most part, however, these models show that transport variables are no more critical to location decisions than such factors as housing type, size, and cost suitability, crime rates, and, for families with children, schools. Moreover life-style and life-cycle variations have been found to be equally important as (in some cases, much more important than) transportation as determinants of location and land use choices.

EMPIRICAL STUDIES AND ISSUES

Given such complexities, can theorized land use and transportation relationships, or those implied by model results, be discerned in the real world? A number of studies have investigated various aspects of the interactions, particularly focusing on the effects of transportation investments on land use, location, and economic development. These studies have used a variety of methodologies, including macroeconomic investigations, econometric analyses, and input-output modeling of national and regional effects. Before-after studies of specific facilities or regions and survey-based research on residential and industrial location choices also have been used.

Many of these empirical studies suffer from methodological and other limitations (lack of explanatory power for observed correlations, difficulty in distinguishing cause and effect, failure to distinguish economic shifts within a region from investment-induced growth, double counting of benefits). Few have been scoped broadly enough to identify possible shifts in production processes and changes in economic and social organization that might occur as a result of important new transportation investments. Nevertheless, the studies offer insights. Overall, they find that transportation availability and quality are factors in location and development, but investments—at least, the modest investments typical of today's transportation programs—will do relatively little absent other critical factors including appropriate land, labor, and capital.

Land Development Effects of Highways

Studies of the land development effects of highway investments have a long and detailed history (*26–31*). Recent studies have been motivated in large part by the interest in using highways as instruments of economic development. However, most studies have found that highway investments are but one factor in a larger growth and development equation (*32*). Some studies have failed to find an impact of any sort, especially in areas with weak markets for development; others have found that highway investments allow pent-up demand for new development to be released. Many of the studies that have attributed "growth" to a new highway have failed to account for the likelihood that growth would have occurred elsewhere in the region had the highway not been developed. A shift, not an increase, is what has occurred (*33*).

Environmentalists sometimes argue that it is precisely this shift that is of concern, in particular if development is induced by transportation improvements to make more trips, make longer trips, or relocate from high-density areas where many trips would be made by foot or transit to low-density areas heavily dependent on the automobile. Newman and Kenworthy (*34*) claim that international data on transportation, land use, and energy consumption establish a strong basis for this concern; among metropolitan planning organizations, scenario-testing exercises and a few modeling efforts using real data have explored this issue sufficiently to support the conclusion that shifts could occur sufficient to offset at least some of transportation investments' initial travel benefits. [See Frank (*35*), among others, for a review of the literature on the transportation, environmental, and other consequences of alternative development patterns; see Harvey (*36*) for a discussion of the modeling issues.]

But the magnitude of the effect remains unclear, and controversy continues over when and to what degree a highway improvement will induce trips, shift modes, and alter destination choices. It seems likely that more detailed consideration of this issue will be required in coming years (*36, 37*).

Land Development Effects of Transit

Can transit investments alter development patterns? Here, the question of shifts is central, because many look to transit to help restructure development into more compact, efficient patterns. Most studies have focused on rail systems, though a few have looked at less place-specific investments such as trolleys on shared right-of-way and bus services (38–43).

The results of the studies are mixed (44–46). Many localized benefits can be found, but from a regional perspective the benefits are quite modest. Shifts toward compact growth and increased density, when they occur, seem overwhelmed by stronger regional trends toward decentralization. Rail systems do seem to have supported additional downtown development, though several also apparently made once-remote suburban locations sufficiently accessible to spur development at the fringe (39, 47).

Overall, the findings on transit are similar to those on highways. Transit availability and quality affect location and land use, but so do many other factors. Unless these other factors are supportive, transit investment will not make a difference in development.

LAND USE AND URBAN DESIGN INTERVENTIONS

So far, the discussion of land use and transportation has focused on location decision processes as a function of transportation and land costs, or on transportation impacts on land use patterns and mixes. The work in these areas draws heavily on an economic conception of urban spatial processes. Most theories of transportation and land use, and most models based on those theories, assume that market forces dominate; they pay little attention to explicit planning and policy interventions, public or private. And when these interventions have been considered by economists, the reaction has been almost entirely negative. Indeed, zoning and other interventions into the operation of land markets have been roundly criticized for artificially restricting development, especially the development of housing for low- and moderate-income households; land regulations have been blamed for higher housing costs and longer commutes.

Yet a variety of planning and policy interventions are being considered as means of improving the management of transportation–land use interactions. Among the interventions receiving the most attention are state and regional planning and programming approaches; creative zoning and other land use regulations (including those techniques collectively called "growth management"), public and private site design regulations, financing and pricing policies, and intergovernmental relations (*48–51*).

Many of these measures are being proposed specifically as means of reducing transportation problems. The most common methods include

• Urban limit lines and urban development reserves designed to produce compact development in areas where urban services are already available or are scheduled;

• Mandatory consistency between local land use plans and local and regional transportation plans;

• Requirements for the provision of adequate public facilities concurrent with development, or attainment of minimum level-of-service standards;

• Mandatory balancing of job growth with housing development, priced and located to match the needs and incomes of the work force;

• Minimum as well as maximum development densities and floor-area ratios to ensure adequate development for transit to work;

• Incentives and bonuses for desired land uses and for developments that provide desired transportation and land use amenities; and

• Site design planning emphasizing pedestrian access and transit serviceability.

Advocates of these techniques believe that they would produce both transportation and land use benefits. Urban limit lines would focus development and encourage efficient use of land; infrastructure costs would be reduced. Joint planning and development of land uses and transportation facilities would avoid many conflicts and capacity problems. Explicit planning for alternatives to the automobile would create supportive environments for their operation and use; improved positioning of work, shopping, educational, recreational, and other facilities relative to residences would reduce trip lengths and make walking and bicycling feasible. In some cases, intensive trip-generating land uses would be concentrated so that high-capacity transit could be deployed successfully; major highway improvements would be foregone and parking restricted to make the automobile less attractive.

Advantages to society overall are thought to include decreased requirements for travel, lower energy consumption, and less air pollution; urban sprawl would be reduced, sparing valued agricultural lands and other open space. Costs also would accrue, but they have received less attention. Theory says that these strategies would tend to favor central locations over other ones, and perhaps raise housing prices in the most accessible locations. In some cases, development would be likely to spill beyond the urban boundaries into unregulated, rural towns, or perhaps would shift to other metropolitan regions.

Empirical evidence on the regionally oriented measures is accumulating (52) but remains too scattered and partial for effective use by policymakers; here is clearly an area for future research. At the smaller scale of urban design, recent projects have attempted to moderate travel demand and influence mode choice through a conscious design process. Assessments of these projects have identified four key underlying dimensions: density, development size, land use mix, and design features (scale, coverage, etc.) have been found to be of use in explaining observed differences in travel patterns, with the first three appearing to be most important (53, 54). Abundant free parking also has been found to be a critical factor in mode choice, favoring drive-alone (55). Yet the variability with other factors—real estate markets, location within the region, demographics, and lifestyle—is substantial and only partially understood. More work will be needed on the stability and replicability of the partial results found to date.

OTHER POLICY AND INSTITUTIONAL ISSUES

Although land use policies have received the most attention, financing and pricing policies also affect transportation and land development in ways both obvious and not so obvious.

Fiscal zoning—zoning in tax ratables and zoning out housing, especially housing for families with children—has become as notorious as it is ubiquitous, though few concrete proposals on how to deter or offset the effects of this practice have been suggested. Regional tax sharing and fair-share housing programs are the strategies most often mentioned, but their acceptability and efficacy, respectively, are in doubt. How fiscal zoning affects transportation, especially the commute to job-rich, housing-restricted suburbs, is only beginning to be explored; early results suggest that low- and moderate-income households may face substantially longer commutes than would be the case in a less restrictive locale.

Other products of the local government fiscal crisis may have a more positive effect: exactions and impact fees may provide the resources to improve transportation conditions. Yet studies suggest that optimism may be misplaced, because impact fees often are a fraction of what would be needed to offset traffic growth or provide meaningful alternatives, and their imposition may worsen housing costs and direct development to fringe/rural areas where growth is relatively unregulated and welcomed.

Tax policies are a third area affecting transportation, land development, and locational patterns. Tax deductions are believed to lead to artificially high levels of consumption of housing; parking exemptions support overconsumption of automobile travel; depreciation rules (along with banking and insurance deregulation) helped support office overbuilding in the 1980s and the subsequent competition for tenants in a soft market. And taxation and pricing of transportation itself, from fuel taxes to toll road policies, have land use as well as transportation implications.

Finally, intergovernmental relations can have a major impact on land use and transportation issues. Currently, land use is predominantly a local government issue; transportation is a shared responsibility of federal and state governments and special districts in which local cities and towns usually play but a minor role. Competition and conflict, with attendant negative spillovers, have led to initiatives in states such as Florida and New Jersey to build new institutional relationships fostering coordination, cooperation, and negotiation. It remains to be seen whether such new governmental arrangements will produce improved outcomes, or whether greater advantages result from the Tiebout (56) world in which fragmentation of local government allows individuals to "vote with their feet" and match government services to their own tastes.

CONCLUSIONS: AREAS FOR FUTURE RESEARCH

The relationships among transportation, land use, and urban form have been much studied, and important conclusions can be drawn from this large body of research. Nevertheless, many questions remain, and there is a need especially for careful attention to matters of method and data, as well as a need for additional research.

Methodological Issues

Several methodological issues become apparent in reviewing theory and evidence about land use–transportation interactions and contrasting what is known or can be analyzed with the policy issues being raised. To start, further elaborations of theoretical models to account explicitly for multinucleation, specialization of places, spatial irregularities, and nonhomogeneous tastes are needed. Such efforts are under way, but more attention and more resources are needed.

Perhaps most notable from an empirical viewpoint is that the issues are not well addressed by most operational land use and transportation models in use today. Theory says that changes in the availability and level of service offered by transportation facilities would affect location choice, trip generation, destination choice, and mode choice. Operational models for the most part lack the recursiveness needed to assess the extent to which such feedback would occur. In this respect they lag behind the state of the art and may even represent regression from earlier periods in which planning and analysis commanded greater attention and resources. In any case, procedures for estimating the effects of transportation on development patterns are needed, as are empirical studies to be used as an evidentiary base.

A related issue concerns data. Without good data, sound analysis results cannot be expected. Yet data problems have hampered most of the studies reported in the literature, and data problems may have worsened since those studies were done. A new round of travel surveying, traffic counting, and other investigations is overdue in most metropolitan areas. Moreover, if serious analyses of transportation–land use interactions are to be carried out, at least some of the data needed must be longitudinal, permitting the analyst to track changes over time. This is particularly true for studies of growth effects that may occur over a 10- to 15-year period.

Research Needs

Questions about how transportation shapes locational choices and supports improved opportunity have moved to the forefront in recent years, along with concerns about potentially negative impacts of transportation investment on air quality and sprawl. Proposals to use transportation to spur economic growth and revitalization, reduce environmental degradation, improve social equity, and increase the quality of the built environment are key policy agenda items. Theory provides useful insights into the likely effects of these policy proposals but is increasingly unable to capture the effects of important changes in structure resulting from economic, social, demographic, and technological change. Empirical work suggests that transportation's role can be important, but better information on the precise nature and magnitude of the effects is needed.

Promising research topics include the following:

• Development and refinement of both conceptual and analytical models of location that account for multinucleation and specialization and reflect demographic and socioeconomic realities;

• Development and refinement of modeling approaches for analyzing land use–transportation interactions, including feedback effects of transportation supply on location and trip making;

• Application of improved theories and models to explore the likely impacts of a variety of transportation and land use policies, including new technologies and alternative public policies;

• Both quantitative and qualitative exploration of the transportation impacts of alternative zoning, growth management, and other land regulation strategies;

• Analysis of the effects of finance and pricing policies on both transportation and land use choices and patterns; and

• Exploration of alternative organizational arrangements and assignments of responsibility and their effects on transportation and land use outcomes.

ACKNOWLEDGMENTS

Development of this paper was supported in part by the University of California Transportation Center. Portions of this paper draw upon a paper written by William Garrison and Elizabeth Deakin for the Institute of Transportation Studies.

REFERENCES

1. J. H. von Thünen. *Der isolierte Staat in Beziehung auf Landwertschaft und Nationalekonomie.* Hamburg, 1826.
2. D. Ricardo. *Principles of Political Economy and Taxation.* London, 1817.
3. E. S. Dunn, Jr. *The Location of Agricultural Production.* University of Florida Press, Gainesville, 1954.
4. W. Isard. *Location and Space-Economy.* M.I.T. Press, Cambridge, Mass., 1956.
5. L. Wingo, Jr., ed. *Cities and Space: The Future Use of Urban Land.* Resources for the Future, The Johns Hopkins Press, Baltimore, 1972.
6. W. Alonso. *Location and Land Use: Toward a General Theory of Land*

    Rents. Joint Center for Urban Studies Publication Series. Harvard University Press, Cambridge, Mass., 1964.
 7. J. F. Kain. The Journey to Work as a Determinant of Residential Location. In *Essays on Urban Spatial Structure* (J. F. Kain, ed.), Ballinger, Cambridge, Mass., 1975.
 8. E. S. Mills. An Aggregate Model of Resource Allocation in a Metropolitan Area. *American Economic Review,* Vol. 57, 1967, pp. 197–210.
 9. A. Anas. Modeling the Dynamic Evolution of Land Use in Response to Transportation Improvement Policies. In *Transportation and Mobility in an Era of Transition* (G. R. M. Jansen, P. Nijkamp, and C. Ruijgrok, eds.), North-Holland, Amsterdam, 1985.
10. E. W. Burgess. The Growth of the City. In *The City: Problems of Planning* (M. Steward, ed.), Penguin Books, Baltimore, 1972.
11. R. M. Hurd. *Principles of City Land Values.* Real Estate Record Association, 1903 (reprint, The Record and Guide, 1924).
12. H. Hoyt. *The Structure and Growth of Residential Neighborhoods in American Cities.* Government Printing Office, Washington, D.C., 1939.
13. C. D. Harris and E. L. Ullman. The Nature of Cities. *Annals of the American Academy of Political and Social Sciences,* November 1945.
14. B. Berry. *Geography of Market Centers and Retail Distribution.* Prentice-Hall, Englewood Cliffs, N.J., 1967.
15. W. G. Alcaly. Transportation and Urban Land Values: A Review of the Theoretical Literature. *Land Economics,* Vol. 52, 1976.
16. G. Giuliano. *New Directions for Understanding Transportation and Land Use.* University of California, Irvine, 1988.
17. I. Lowry. *A Model of Metropolis.* Rand, Santa Monica, Calif., 1964.
18. S. H. Putman. *Integrated Urban Models.* Pion, London, 1983.
19. F. Ducca and S. Putman. *A Guide to Using DRAM, EMPAL, CALIB.* University of Pennsylvania, Philadelphia, 1978.
20. J. P. Herbert and B. H. Stevens. A Model for Distribution of Residential Activities in Urban Areas. *Journal of Regional Science,* Vol. 2, No. 2, 1960.
21. P. Prastacos. An Integrated Land Use Transportation Model for the San Francisco Region. *Environment and Planning,* Vol. 18, 1985.
22. J. Hamburg, E. J. Kaiser, and G. T. Lathrop. *NCHRP Report 266: Forecasting Inputs to Transportation Planning.* TRB, National Research Council, Washington, D.C., 1983.
23. J. Berechman and K. Small. *Modelling Land Use and Transportation: An Interpretive Review for Growth Areas.* Institute of Transportation Studies, University of California, Irvine, 1987.
24. J. Bajpai. *NCHRP Report 328: Forecasting the Basic Inputs to Transportation Planning at the Zonal Level.* TRB, National Research Council, Washington, D.C., June 1990.
25. S. R. Lerman. Location, Housing, Automobile Ownership, and Mode to Work: A Joint Choice Model. In *Transportation Research Record 610,* TRB, National Research Council, Washington, D.C., 1975.
26. U.S. Congress. House. *Progress Report of the Highway Cost Allocation Study.* 85th Cong., 1st Sess., March 4, 1957. H. Doc. 106.
27. U.S. Congress. House. *Progress Report of the Highway Cost Allocation Study.* 85th Cong., 2nd Sess., March 3, 1958. H. Doc. 344.
28. U. S. Congress. House. *Progress Report of the Highway Cost Allocation Study.* 86th Cong., 1st Sess., 1959. H. Doc. 91.

29. U.S. Congress. House. *Progress Report of the Highway Cost Allocation Study.* 86th Cong., 2nd Sess., 1960. H. Doc. 355.

30. U.S. Congress. House. *Final Report of the Highway Cost Allocation Study.* 87th Cong., 1st Sess., January 16, 1961. H. Doc. 54.

31. U.S. Congress. House. *Final Report of the Highway Cost Allocation Study, Part VI: Studies of the Economic and Social Effects of Highway Improvement.* 87th Cong., 1st Sess., January 23, 1961. H. Doc. 72.

32. Payne-Maxie Consultants and Blayney-Dyett Associates. *The Land Use and Urban Development Impacts of Beltways.* U.S. Department of Transportation and U.S. Department of Housing and Urban Development, Washington, D.C., 1980.

33. D. J. Forkenbrock, T. F. Pogue, N. S. J. Foster, and D. J. Finnegan. *Road Investment to Foster Local Economic Development.* Iowa University Public Policy Center, Iowa City, May 1990.

34. P. W. G. Newman and J. R. Kenworthy. *Cities and Automobile Dependence: A Sourcebook.* Gower, Brookfield, Vt., 1989.

35. J. E. Frank. *The Cost of Alternative Development Patterns: A Review of the Literature.* Urban Land Institute, Washington, D.C., 1989.

36. G. W. Harvey. *Declaration in Support of MTC's Revised Conformity Procedures.* U.S. District Court for the Northern District of California, Civil No. C-89-2044-TEH/C-89-2064-TEH (Consolidated), June 1990.

37. J. H. Suhrbier and E. Deakin. Environmental Considerations in a 2020 Transportation Plan—Constraints or Opportunities? In *Special Report 220: A Look Ahead: Year 2020.* TRB, National Research Council, Washington, D.C., 1988.

38. E. H. Spengler. *Land Values in New York in Relation to Transit Facilities.* Columbia University Press, New York, N.Y., 1930.

39. S. B. Warner. *Streetcar Suburbs.* Aetheneum, New York, N.Y., 1962.

40. D. E. Boyce, B. Allen, R. R. Mudge, P. B. Slater, and A. M. Isserman. *Impact of Rapid Transit on Suburban Residential Property Values and Land Development.* U.S. Department of Transportation, Office of the Secretary; University of Pennsylvania; Wharton School of Finance and Commerce, Philadelphia, November 1972.

41. R. Cervero. Light Rail Transit and Urban Development. *Journal of the American Planning Association,* Spring 1984.

42. C. A. Gannon and M. J. Dear. *The Impact of Rail Rapid Transit Systems on Commercial Office Development: The Case of the Philadelphia-Lindenwold Speedline.* UMTA; University of Pennsylvania, Philadelphia, June 1972.

43. G. W. Heenan. The Economic Effect of Rapid Transit on Real Estate Development. *Appraisal Journal,* Vol. 36, No. 2, April 1968.

44. R. L. Knight and L. L. Trygg. *Land Use Impacts of Rapid Transit: Implications of Recent Experience.* U.S. Department of Transportation, Office of the Secretary; De Leuw, Cather & Company, San Francisco, August 1977.

45. M. C. Libicki. *Land Use Impacts of Major Transit Improvements.* U.S. Department of Transportation, Office of the Secretary, Washington, D.C., March 1975.

46. G. Giuliano. Land Use Impacts of Transportation Investments: Highways and Transit. In *The Geography of Urban Transportation* (S. Hansen, ed.), Guilford Press, New York, 1986.

47. M. W. Webber. The BART Experience—What Have We Learned? *The Public Interest,* No. 45 (Fall 1976), pp. 79–108.

48. E. Deakin. Growth Controls and Growth Management: Empirical Evidence.

In *Understanding Growth Management* (D. Porter, ed.), Urban Land Institute, Washington, D.C., 1989.

49. E. Deakin. The Politics of Exactions. In *Private Supply of Public Services* (R. Alterman, ed.), New York University Press, 1988.

50. E. Deakin. *State Programs for Managing Land Use, Growth, and Fiscal Impact*. California Senate Office of Research, 1989.

51. E. Deakin. Land Use and Transportation Planning in Response to Congestion Problems: A Review and Critique. In *Transportation Research Record 1237*, TRB, National Research Council, Washington, D.C., 1989.

52. T. Baerwald. Land Use Change in Suburban Clusters and Corridors. In *Transportation Research Record 861*, TRB, National Research Council, Washington, D.C., 1982.

53. R. Cervero. *America's Urban Centers: A Study of the Land Use Transportation Link*. Unwin Hyman, Boston, 1989.

54. B. S. Pushkarev and J. Zupan. *Public Transportation and Land Use Policy*. Indiana University Press, Bloomington, 1977.

55. D. Shoup. Cashing Out Free Parking. *Transportation Quarterly*, 1981.

56. C. M. Tiebout. A Pure Theory of Local Expenditures. *Journal of Political Economy*, Vol. 64, October 1956, pp. 416–424.

Does Transportation Finance Influence Urban Form?

JEFFREY A. PARKER

Jeffrey A. Parker & Associates, Washington, D.C.

There is no "silver bullet" solution to ameliorating the by-products of inadequate and inefficient public sector investment in transportation facilities. In recent years, public policy and the literature have given much emphasis to increasing private sector participation in transportation facilities. Techniques to blend public and private resources optimally, as well as to create incentives for rational project design and selection, are needed. This paper is written from the perspective of a practitioner in the field, rather than as a scholarly review. As a result, it tends to draw observations from experience more than from the current literature. These experiences include serving as a principal in a large urban office development, a land developer (perhaps speculator is more appropriate) in suburban locations, a consultant to public agencies on project finance and policy, and a strategic planning analyst for public transportation agencies.

The first section considers the relationships between transportation and financing factors on land use. The second explores recent experiences with private sector financing. The final section raises questions pertaining to allocating available resources and establishing directions for future research.

THE EVOLVING TRANSPORTATION–LAND USE LINKAGE

As the many highway interchanges that have yet to attract a convenience store or the many rail stations surrounded by vacant lots indicate, a host of factors influence the location and form of development in addition to transportation capacity and the means to finance it.

This personal observation finds confirmation in a limited review of recent studies. In Giuliano's excellent literature synthesis, there are several supporting conclusions (*1*, pp. 16, 19):

> Today's metropolitan areas are characterized by a well developed transportation system and a highly decentralized pattern of land use. These characteristics have reduced accessibility-related differences between locations, which have in turn weakened the transportation–land use linkage.
>
> . . . The transportation system in most urban areas is highly developed. The relative impact of even major investments (for example, a new freeway segment) on accessibility is generally minor, and therefore their impact on urban form will likely be minor as well.

Giuliano finds that declining transportation costs have resulted in more dispersed urban development and that the scattering of both jobs and housing has reduced the significance of transportation in location decisions of households and firms. More important, even substantial increases in transportation costs were not expected to alter the decentralization process, and were anticipated to be offset by shifts in travel patterns and technological advances.

If the transportation–land use linkage is weakening as a result of the maturing, high-quality access network, then the value of particular transportation improvements to a private entity will not be as great and the willingness (or ability) to enter into cost-sharing arrangements will be reduced as a consequence.

In an assessment of the influence of road investment on economic development, the Public Policy Center of the University of Iowa and the Midwest Transportation Center (*2*) reviewed a number of studies that reached parallel conclusions (*2*, pp. 29, 32, 34, 35, 39):

• Transportation investment may be a necessary but not a sufficient factor for economic development.

• The impact of highway investments today, with a mature highway system, may not be the same as in earlier periods.

• Proximity to a metropolitan area was a better predictor of nonmetropolitan county growth than the presence of major highways.

• The presence of highways had very weak impacts in less developed rural areas.

• Relationships between highways and local development were mainly by association—there was little confidence that highways led to growth, rather than vice versa.

• The economic development process is too complex and the role of transportation is not likely to be sufficiently dominant to allow causal relationships to be established.

- Education, unionization, physical amenities, business climate, energy, and tax rates define a region's developmental prospects to a much greater extent than do highways.

It is important to note that one of the principal conclusions of the University of Iowa investigation was (2, p. 29):

> . . . rarely will the high construction costs of adding new regional highways to the nation's highway system be justified, even in less developed areas. A sufficient number of developable sites remain that providing highway access to others is unlikely to advance economic development.

The down side of inefficient resource allocation decisions and improper needs assessments also was observed (2, p. 25):

> Investing public funds in highway projects that are not efficient can actually reduce an area's economic development potential. . . . If the cost savings [attributable to the transportation investment] do not exceed the expense necessary to construct and operate a highway, the highway and the increase in taxes and/or user charges that it entails make the area less attractive to mobile resources.

The first set of conclusions tends to minimize the causal effects of transportation improvements on development and indicates a declining value increment attributable to specific transportation projects on adjacent real estate. These findings are consistent with Giuliano's and suggest that expectations for future private sector contributions must be tempered by generally declining marginal benefits of new transportation facilities.

The latter observation regarding the need for solid capital budgeting discipline tends to run counter to the trend toward politicizing the investment decision making process. Investments in facilities that are not necessary or in excess of actual requirements divert funds from high-benefit projects and impose serious opportunity costs. These impacts include artificial constraints on market-supported growth prospects, a long-term fiscal drag from unnecessary maintenance and depreciation costs, and the use of higher-cost (in terms of the cost of capital) private sector solutions to meet priority needs. Building lower-benefit projects still requires imposition of broadly based taxes and user fees that reduce regional competitiveness if not offset by tangible gains in mobility and productivity. Misallocation of resources can occur between jurisdictions (diverting funding from areas experiencing real travel demands to areas where transportation projects are intended to exert a "pump priming" influence), as well as within jurisdictions (improper project selections or overinvestment in particular facilities).

Kenworthy and Newman (3) analyzed gasoline use and the resulting pollution impacts in 32 cities located within the United States, Europe, and the Pacific Rim. They discerned a consistent relationship between various measures of urban form (land use intensity, degree of concentration), transportation system characteristics (automobile ownership, availability of parking, availability of public transit service, amount of roadway space), and energy consumption.

Of interest was the absence of an observed link between the wide variety of transportation financing mechanisms used in the cities studied and urban form. The critical determinants of land use–transportation interactions were feedback loops involving public policy decisions on land use, development densities, parking availability, roadway capacity, and the balancing of transit and highway investments. In fact, the study found evidence that applying highway level-of-service criteria to determine the adequacy of facilities would reinforce trends toward dispersion and automobile dependency. The conclusion is a call for greater attention to a balanced transit and highway investment policy, with supportive land use controls.

These findings reinforce the view that it may be more important to make proper decisions about how and where to spend funds than how to raise them. Similarly, with a mature transportation system in place, land use planning and market processes exert stronger influences on urban form than do transportation finance considerations.

Several recent articles on future development trends reinforce these observations on the land use–transportation linkage. If cities continue to expand their boundaries indefinitely and develop more and more new urban cores, the resulting pattern of dispersion will tend to drive future transportation investments. However, market and political forces seem to be suggesting that this is not likely to be the case and that "in-fill" of current metropolitan boundaries is a more probable outcome. A recent review of development trends in the coming decade by Leinberger (4) anticipates a slowdown in outward expansion of urbanized areas driven by the search for cheap land. From a market perspective, Leinberger sees broad availability of sites at all price ranges within current metropolitan boundaries because of the geometric expansion that has occurred over the past 20 years. This view corresponds with the conclusions presented earlier from the Guiliano (1) and University of Iowa (2) studies, suggesting that the declining marginal development benefits would be derived from further expansions of the highway network.

Leinberger also anticipates that the weak market forces pushing further outward will be blocked by strengthened political initiatives to manage growth and preserve open spaces. These trends will tend to define urban form more than transportation financing techniques will, and suggest the need for better tools to determine where transportation investments should occur and what character they should assume.

As a peripheral observation, it is in fringe locations, where the basic price of land has been sufficiently low and the cost of transportation improvements still modestly priced, that developers in recent years have been able to justify economically what appear to be significant proffers for infrastructure. More limited outward expansion could reduce future opportunities for private projects and increase the need for public-private cost-sharing mechanisms.

New approaches to development also have the potential to minimize transportation requirements and influence urban form directly. Perhaps most significant among these trends is the "traditional neighborhood" approach, which appears to yield substantial traffic reduction benefits (5). These site planning and project development approaches do have implications for transportation finance, but more from the perspective of the amount and nature of transport capacity required rather than from the suggestion of particular financing techniques.

The interaction between public and private capital investments in transportation facilities bears consideration as part of the review of evolving land use–transportation linkages. From the standpoint of sheer dollars generated, the bulk of funding to pay for transportation investments comes from broadly based sources—gas taxes, sales taxes, general fund contributions, vehicle registration fees, and so forth. FHWA has estimated that more than $19 billion will be spent on the federal-aid system in FY 1992, with about one-fourth coming from state sources (6). The transit industry spends about $15 billion per year on operations, with about one-third derived from operations and the balance from state, local, and federal sources (7). The incidence of these broad-based mechanisms tends to affect national (in the case of the federal gas tax) or regional economic forces, rather than specific sites and their form of development. However, even though we have concluded a weakening land use–transportation linkage, expenditure of the proceeds of broad-based financing mechanisms on large scale improvements will have some impact on specific locations.

As a result, relatively small private sector shares can, in many cases, "leverage" much larger investments of public funds. As long as broadly based financing sources constitute the primary streams of transportation investment capital, the role of private sector capital will remain on the margin. However, allowing the availability of private resources to exert a high degree of leverage in targeting much larger amounts of public funds has the potential either to exacerbate underlying inefficiencies in the capital budgeting process or to act as a guiding factor in directing funds to projects with significant immediate benefits. These divergent possibilities reinforce the need for more sophisticated capital budgeting techniques for project selection and scoping.

In concluding that the means of financing transportation improvements plays a less significant role in defining urban form than do market and regulatory forces, it is necessary to recognize one area in which local government financing mechanisms may be contributing to poor land use decisions and to transportation problems. On the basis of personal experiences in buying and attempting to sell property in outlying areas of high-growth markets, the attraction of many rural areas undergoing initial development has been low-cost land for residential development. In cases where market trends yielded successful residential development, the unfortunate result was demand for costly public services—schools, public safety, libraries, and so forth. Bedroom jurisdictions quickly realized that commercial development was needed to generate property and sales taxes to keep overall tax rates reasonable and still satisfy service demands. As the red carpet for retail, industrial, and commercial development was rolled out, a combination of ad hoc siting, zoning, and development decisions manifested itself in congestion, among other problems.

Caught between the need for tax revenues and the possibility of seeing attractive commercial development locate in adjacent communities, many outlying counties now find themselves in a traffic dilemma. It is possible that regional tax base sharing, regional planning of infrastructure, and regional financing mechanisms could reduce the pressures for tax base competition that may be an underlying factor leading to poor land use decision making and growing transportation demands.

PRIVATE SECTOR PARTICIPATION IN TRANSPORTATION FINANCE

It has been traditional for commercial, industrial, and residential land developers to pay for site-specific improvements, such as parking and internal streets. In recent years, off-site improvements to upgrade regional facilities and joint developments involving public-private partnerships have emerged as new directions for financing transportation systems.

As the federal highway system has moved toward completion, fewer and fewer miles of costly regional capacity have been brought on stream using the most broad-based financing tool, the Highway Trust Fund. Tax limitation pressures have caused broad-based sources of state and local revenue to lag behind infrastructure investment requirements. The result of these trends has been to place increased pressure on project-specific revenue sources—fees, assessments, and proffers. The evolution of private sector participation, therefore, can be viewed partially as a response to growth-related politics, inadequate tax revenue, and the legal and economic inability of land use regulation to meet popular expectations.

Because of the feverish pace of construction and rapid escalation in land costs in the United States over the past decade, private interests were able to absorb a high level of nontraditional, off-site infrastructure costs, allowing the new approaches to achieve positive results in satisfying public and private needs. Encouraged by imprudently allocated capital were more than a few cases in which the front-end carrying costs necessitated by otherwise public sector investments have helped bring private developments to insolvency. The cost for such off-site regional transportation investments may yet be borne at the federal level; however, the Resolution Trust Corporation rather than the Highway Trust Fund will be debited.

Joint development permits the value created by transportation investments to be shared and plowed back into financing the public portion of the project. It too has enjoyed considerable attention as a financing mechanism, and one that has the potential to influence urban form by concentrating densities at major transportation hubs. Market conditions have affected projects with heavy reliance on joint development as well.

The greatest potential for using project-specific revenue sources occurs in high-growth locations where inadequate funding from conventional sources for regional transportation facilities has contributed to a run-up in land values through constraints imposed under the entitlement and environmental review process. The large "delta" between raw land and entitled sites resulting from negotiated transportation investments is the basis for value-sharing arrangements. Developer contributions can be maximized by combining project-specific financing mechanisms with an accelerated entitlement process. The down side to applying private sector-oriented financing mechanisms involves tolerating high levels of interim congestion to create pent-up demand, the evolution of a "density for sale" zoning orientation, and a high degree of market sensitivity.

The ability of project-specific financing mechanisms to address rehabilitation and reconstruction needs remains to be determined on a broader scale. At present, the leading example of rehabilitation-oriented public-private partnerships is New York City. Extensive improvements to subway stations have been negotiated through the entitlement process, and it appears that even Donald Trump may help in relocating the decayed Miller Highway. However, the forces of growth are not always strong in areas with extensive reconstruction needs. It is important that the shift in transportation priorities toward rehabilitating existing facilities not leave us formulating tomorrow's solutions based on yesterday's problems.

The needs of a mature transportation system may require different approaches to eliciting private sector participation and could have different implications for influencing urban form. Perhaps the greatest concern is that generating the funds to rebuild the infrastructure of developed areas not chase away jobs and housing from established cities and older suburbs.

The following discussion examines some of the land use benefits and limitations of newer, private-sector-oriented transportation financing tools.

FINANCING MECHANISMS AS PART OF THE REGULATORY PROCESS

The imposition of impact fees, special assessments, and proffers has been woven into the politics of growth management. The willingness of the public to pay for transportation improvements necessitated by growth and changing patterns of travel demand is never high. This fact of life often gives rise to the solution that the forces of growth should pay their own way. A frequent corollary is that restricting transportation investment somehow will limit growth.

In fact, there is no free lunch that allows the private sector to absorb the costs of needed public investment. The reality is that private forces cannot sustain all of the carrying costs of infrastructure required by new development. Land economics and market forces have combined in recent years to demonstrate that matching land sales and absorption forecasts is not an exact science and that large, front-end carrying costs are a primary factor in real estate financial failures. On the other hand, restricting transportation capacity in and of itself will only begin to deter growth at truly intolerable levels of congestion, if at all. One need only experience traffic congestion and transit overcrowding in Tokyo, Paris, Singapore, Bangkok, Brussels, or London (or Orange County, California) to test this hypothesis. The levels of road and transit service routinely tolerated in these cities would not be accepted in the United States but amply demonstrate that shutting down transportation capacity alone will not stop growth.

It should be noted that tax mechanisms can be used to shape urban form when they are consciously applied as a regulatory tool in conjunction with explicit land use policies. For example, in Japan and some European countries, capital gains and inheritance taxes are set at almost confiscatory levels when land is sold or removed from agricultural use. The net effect is to limit suburbanization and grossly inflate the value of urban land available for development. Urban congestion, crowded offices and apartments, and sky-high rents are frequent by-products. Similar effects could be achieved in the United States if these measures were adopted. However, such drastic tax strategies are unlikely to be supported in the United States, and the life-style changes they would trigger are inconsistent with trends in housing and commercial development since World War II. The use of extreme tax policies to achieve regulatory objectives also is inconsistent with transportation financing requirements, because the primary purpose is to discourage certain changes in land use rather than to generate a predictable revenue stream.

Less drastic transactional measures, such as real estate–related taxes in New York City levied on behalf of the Metropolitan Transportation Authority, are used to support transportation services in the United States. However, they are subject to sudden declines during periods of market retrenchment (8) and must be blended into a larger financing package that includes more stable sources of revenue.

Several mechanisms have been incorporated into the land use/growth management process to finance transportation projects. These approaches are briefly examined below.

Impact Fees

The use of impact fees is growing as an infrastructure financing mechanism (9), and the amount charged is increasing as well. A *Growth Management Studies Newsletter* (10) reported that the national average for road-related impact fees was more than $1,500 per single family housing unit, more than $1,800 per 1,000 ft^2 of office space, and almost $2,300 per 1,000 ft^2 of retail space. However, impact fees (covering multiple public purposes) of more than $15,000 per housing unit are reported in California, a significant proportion of which is no doubt going toward roads. Fees can influence housing costs and land values; however, outside of a few unusual circumstances involving large-scale community developments under common ownership, they generally are not sufficiently high in relation to selling prices to constitute a major distortion of market forces. If applied in well-developed suburban or urbanized areas, the biased incidence of impact fees on new projects could tend to artificially inflate the value of the existing building stock.

If impact fees were relied on as the basic source of transportation funding, they would quickly reach unsustainable levels—particularly if improvements to regional facilities are considered. The fluctuation of fee revenues with market trends further reduces their attractiveness as a stable source of funding. The literature involving the implications of impact fees on housing costs and neighborhood diversity has not been explored; however, financing transportation improvements through this mechanism may have broader social and economic spinoffs that could feed back into transportation needs. For example, if heavy reliance on transportation impact fees boosts housing prices in a locality, lower-income workers may be forced to live in other areas, increasing commuting needs and offsetting benefits from roads funded by the fees. In many jurisdictions, there are also legal constraints that affect the ability of impact fees to fund major transportation investments. In these cases, impact fees must be used to mitigate transportation demands imposed by the particular development making the payment. In Florida's Broward and Palm Beach counties, the proceeds of impact fee collections are divided among dozens of trust accounts, none of which may have adequate balances to undertake a project. Unless the trust fund balances are expended within a fixed time frame, they must be refunded. The results may be negative influences on land and housing prices, without offsetting benefits in transportation. The spot improvements the fees finance in these cases will neither solve a corridor transportation need nor provide a boost in capacity on a regional facility.

Impact fees, therefore, may best serve as a supplement to other, diverse sources of revenue. This approach is used to support public transit in San Francisco. However, attempting to use impact fees as the principal source of funding for a transportation investment is not likely to succeed because of market swings and legal constraints. Such a strategy also might face successful legal challenge because of adverse impacts on underlying land values.

Proffers

In high-growth areas that have failed to provide adequate public resources for transportation, the private sector frequently has agreed to the use of proffers as a means to accelerate the entitlement process. Trading specific road or transit improvements for entitlements has become a well-established element of environmental reviews in many jurisdictions. Historically, contributions of rights-of-way for highway improvement are common and are a form of proffer. However, excessive reliance on proffers may yield results that are not totally satisfactory from either a development or transportation perspective. Current market conditions have deeply affected the ability of the private sector to make proffers or, in some cases, to deliver on existing commitments. In one sign of the times, the Resolution Trust Corporation has repudiated letters of credit issued by a number of the savings and loan institutions it has taken over that were posted by developers required to make proffered transportation improvements.

The success of a proffer system depends on the availability of adequate public funding for improvements to fill the gaps between projects and to upgrade regional facilities that must accommodate increased local traffic flows. Proffered transportation improvements are likely to be discontinuous, resulting in lane drops, variable traffic patterns, and isolated segments. Essential projects needed to unclog regional travel may go unfunded, whereas pieces of facilities unlikely to be connected to major routes for years may suddenly appear on farms and woodlands. In Fairfax County, Virginia, the developers of the Fair Oaks project recently completed a costly segment of the Fairfax Parkway, but commuters still await public funding decisions for $300 million worth of construction required to complete the roadway. Similar incongruities have been observed in mass transit, where proffered station improvements may occur at relatively low-priority locations and stand in stark contrast to larger, systemic rehabilitation needs.

Proffers may also be contributing to more dispersed development patterns as developers bargain for and receive entitlements that permit them to leapfrog choke points, contrary zoning boards, competitors, or hold-out property owners.

The ability of private developers to carry the cost of off-site infrastructure improvements is a function of market demand and the basic price of land relative to selling prices. For example, the developers of Fair Oaks have reported that under current market conditions the cost of building their segment of the Fairfax Parkway would not have been economically feasible. Failure to achieve a large enough jump in land value as a result of the completed improvement and development entitlements and the inability to close enough land sales at anticipated prices within projected time frames are the risk factors faced by developers making proffers. Unfortunately, the risks tend to be best managed when public investment in transportation is well below requirements and when the supply of entitlements relative to demand is heavily restricted.

It is a legitimate public policy issue whether a locality has to "shoot itself in the foot" by underinvesting in infrastructure and distorting development economics through the entitlement process before the "cure" of proffers becomes sustainable. Lying at the heart of the dilemma is often the unwillingness of local governments, homeowners, or business interests to accept the unavoidable costs of growth through higher taxes. At the same time, the success of proffers still rests on the public sector's financial capacity to close the gaps between spot improvements that are negotiated. Failure by the public sector to deliver on connecting investments can result in worsening travel conditions, despite the private sector's fulfillment of its proffered obligations.

Special Assessments

Developers in western Fairfax County, Virginia, agreed to pay 80 percent of the $120 million cost to widen Route 28 through creation of a special taxing district. Property owners in downtown Denver pay for the cost of maintaining a transit mall through a special assessment program. In Miami, commercial property owners agreed to pay a special assessment to underwrite the local share of a downtown people-mover system and its subsequent extension. A municipal utility district has been used in Los Colinas, Texas, to finance a people-mover system. An analysis of the use of special assessment districts by Rice Center (11) shows an increasing tendency to employ this technique in financing major transportation improvements.

Consensus among landowners is the critical factor in implementing a special assessment program successfully. Recent efforts to construct a fixed guideway system in Denver were derailed by opposition to a special tax during a period of economic retrenchment. Repeated attempts to impose a special assessment program around stations in support of heavy-rail construction in Los Angeles have been thwarted in the courts.

These observations suggest that in high-growth areas with major assemblages of property or with multiple property owners possessing generally compatible aims, special assessments can work well. Although most often combined with extensive public sector funding, in certain cases sufficient revenue streams can be generated to support a complete investment, rather than a spot improvement. These situations are often perceived by the private sector as opportunities to finance needed infrastructure investments from tax-exempt sources. Long-term financings based on special fees frequently are dependent on guarantees from public entities, which can be difficult to secure. The impacts on land use patterns are likely to be limited because of the relatively low levels of assessment involved.

Special assessments should be differentiated from tax increment financings, such as the transportation improvement district approach adopted in Pennsylvania and being used to fund an interchange near Greater Pittsburgh International Airport. Few localities are willing or able to forgo property tax revenues in order to fund transportation projects. Redevelopment powers are often involved, and the proceeds of tax increment financings are more likely to be used for land assembly, on-site improvements, parking, and amenities than for transportation projects normally viewed as state or federal responsibilities.

Public-Private Partnerships

The Florida High Speed Rail Corporation proposed to build a multi-billion-dollar Swedish-technology, electrified railway from Tampa to Miami using real estate development revenues. Transit projects in New York City, Minneapolis, Honolulu, Houston, and other places have been proposed that involve "super-turnkey" implementation that incorporates the proceeds from land sales, density bonuses, accelerated entitlements, and other real estate development benefits into the bid price for the project. A major rail station and interchange point has been proposed in the New Jersey Meadowlands at Allied Junction that would be privately financed. The author even proposed to build a people-mover system from Three Rivers Stadium in Pittsburgh across the Allegheny River into the Golden Triangle in exchange for more than 1 million ft^2 of development rights. To date, none of these offers have been realized. The reasons for lack of progress in this area are economic and market-related, as the following examples demonstrate.

The Washington, D.C., transit agency, the Washington Metropolitan Area Transit Authority (WMATA), operates perhaps the finest heavy-rail system in the world and has one of the most successful joint development programs in the United States. It has entered into land leases with developers for air rights and other projects whose collective value is hundreds of millions of dollars. Washington is one of the nation's premiere real estate markets, with downtown land values estimated in excess of $1,500 per ft^2 in various locations. Its rail-served suburbs in Fairfax County, Virginia; Montgomery County, Maryland; and Prince Georges County, Maryland, are among the most desirable development locations in the United States. WMATA's annual budget (bus and rail) is $668 million, and joint development revenues contribute about $5 million per year. The rail system has been operating for more than a decade, and the build-up of joint development revenues has been gradual. In addition, WMATA supports a full-time staff to manage its joint development activities and has invested heavily in consulting services to maximize the value of its land assets.

These numbers are intended to place expectations for the potential role of joint development in perspective. Their purpose is not to discourage joint development as an element of project financing but only to place its revenue-generating potential in context. WMATA has achieved cost savings in constructing and operating its system as a result of public-private cooperation that do not appear in the previous numbers, and its joint development activities have yielded increased ridership, passenger amenities, jobs, more efficient land use patterns, and large property and sales tax gains for the local jurisdictions. However, transportation projects require cash payments to contractors, and the cash flow implications of joint development must be assessed realistically.

New York has invested more than $12 billion in reconstruction of its subway system over the past decade. During this period, an incentive program offering a 20 percent density bonus has been provided by the city in certain Manhattan locations, and developers have had to make extensive transit improvements as part of the city's environmental review process. With some of the highest property values and most arduous land use review processes in the United States, New York's program has generated about $120 million in privately funded station improvements. One urban redevelopment project now working its way through the last of 55 lawsuits is anticipated to yield more than $50 million in improvements to the Times Square subway complex. The success of New York's joint development program has been a function of the availability of state, city, and federal funds to acquire the rail cars and make track, shop, yard, and other improvements that have permitted a systemwide upgrading to occur. Reliance on certain real estate revenues also has slowed the program, as the continued failure to close the anticipated sale of the Coliseum property (originally because of successful legal challenges and now because of market conditions) has opened a hole in the capital budget of several hundred million dollars.

As Florida's High Speed Rail Program has experienced, the real estate market fluctuates, and few developers or landowners can make firm commitments into the future. The timing of joint development cash flows rarely coincides with the cash requirements of transportation construction projects. The magnitude of dollars that development projects can contribute toward transportation projects is constrained by market economics. Even massive sales of density by public agencies can be thwarted by market trends and the inability to economically justify building out all of the square footage a bonus program may yield. For example, the original economics of the author's proposed Three Rivers Stadium project in Pittsburgh called for construction of three towers of 500,000 ft^2 each. Analysis of subsequent market activity suggested that such large towers could not be leased quickly enough to be economically feasible, and that buildings half the size might be more appropriate. The reduced density limited the potential value that could be tapped to help pay for an associated people-mover system.

Tying transportation investments to land development projects can result in compounding risks and the distinct possibility that a needed transportation project will be placed on hold because of considerations totally removed from underlying travel requirements. On the other hand, transportation investments whose justification is based on future growth projections, such as the Hudson River Waterfront Transitway in New Jersey, are appropriately linked to realizing development build-out milestones.

Proposals for innovative procurement methods that incorporate public-private partnerships, such as super-turnkey and build-operate-transfer, may have the potential to reduce project costs through improved construction management and planning, as well as through accelerated implementation. However, in order to attract private "equity," development-related risks must be recognized, and public sector guarantees will be required in most cases in order to underwrite the long-term revenue risks involved.

Private toll road proposals also may be considered in this category. In many cases, the proposals are growth-driven and arise from a shortfall in public funding. Corridors in Northern Virginia and Orange County, California, are likely to experience strong use at relatively high toll rates because of capacity constraints on free roadways. Land donations are an important economic feasibility factor. A substantial portion of the financing package supporting the projects being built by the Transportation Corridor Agencies near Irvine, California, is being derived from impact fees and assessments. Value created by the highways will be used to help pay their costs; however, the inability of public agencies to provide adequate transportation capacity is the underlying basis for a private sector approach. It remains to be determined if the higher cost of capital for these projects will be offset by private sector construction and operating efficiencies. The administration's proposal to underwrite preliminary engineering costs and permit up to 35 percent of the cost of toll road construction to be federally funded could go far in reducing the risk premiums that investors in private infrastructure projects will require.

In summary, mechanisms to achieve public-private partnerships are a fruitful and important element of an overall strategy to finance transportation investments. However, their ability to substitute for an adequate level of public financing is not unlimited, and much of the value being shared is the result of market distortions caused by inadequate public investment.

FUTURE RESEARCH DIRECTIONS: CAPITAL BUDGETING AND CONSUMER PREFERENCES

There are important opportunities to attract private sector investment to transportation projects, and there is also a need to allocate available capital among projects properly. In assessing current transportation finance issues and their relationship to land use, it appears that more attention has been given to different mechanisms for raising funds than to how available funds are spent. It is the spending side of the equation where the interactions with land use may be more significant, and where the potential for a real leap in productivity and efficiency may be possible. There are also important opportunities to devise and deploy technologies that can yield services that support consumer preferences for dispersed development patterns.

With greater emphasis now being placed on intermodalism, private sector involvement, environmental sensitivity, regional planning, and the upgrading of technological solutions to transportation needs, greater attention to the capital budgeting process and new types of transport services could not be more timely.

For too long, federal funds have been viewed as "free money" by agencies fortunate enough to secure congressional earmarks or when operating and maintenance dollars are limited but capital funds from grants or bonds are readily available. The perverse incentives built in to the categorical nature of transit and highway projects in terms of matching shares, eligible uses of funds, and other factors cannot be overlooked and it is proposed that they be altered in forthcoming reauthorization of surface transportation programs. Tax and debt limitations imposed on state and local governments can induce financing structures that lack justification in economic terms. Finally, difficulties in properly recognizing capital consumption have led to enormous, unfunded depreciation liabilities coinciding with needs for capacity expansion and new services.

These considerations point to a requirement for more sophisticated and rigorous capital budgeting processes, if the benefits of available public and private dollars for transportation investment are to be realized. The most positive influence on land use would be to allocate capital among transportation projects so as to minimize the opportunity costs of paying for public and private investments that fail to respond adequately to real, systemic priorities. Recent proposals to establish congestion, bridge, and pavement management systems, as well as to coordinate transportation and air quality planning, are important elements of this process. In addition, suggested requirements for equitable allocation of funds within states are also essential for maximizing the benefits of transportation investments. The earlier findings regarding the limited benefits and potential costs arising from future expansion of the rural highway system need to be translated into a meaningful analytical framework that can restrain the historic tendencies of many state legislatures and departments of transportation in their allocation decisions.

Parallel to this effort must be a reevaluation of how needs are assessed and quantified. If transportation needs are being caused by an undisciplined land use planning process, how can this condition be evaluated fairly and acted on in federal, state, and local allocation processes?

Technological advancements in maintenance systems do not seem to exert influence on either the manning requirements or the numbers of costly bus and rail shops. Overbuilt road solutions designed for 20-year planning horizons must be balanced against immediate congestion problems in cities and suburbs. Preservation of underused bus routes and rail facilities exaggerates operating expenses and capital needs estimates when rehabilitation costs must be incurred. Determining highway needs based on unmitigated single-occupant automobile travel demand projections or transit needs based on the requirements of the highest-cost alternative will not lead to efficient allocation decisions. Indeed, planning tools that can create integrated transportation solutions (rather than highway or transit) will be required if the promise of flexibility in proposed legislation is to be fulfilled. The result of these efforts must be to minimize the large opportunity costs being borne regionally, and ultimately nationally, by permitting distorted perceptions of needs to drive investment decisions.

Capital budgeting systems employed at the Southern Pennylvania Transportation Authority in Philadelphia and the Metropolitan Transportation Commission in Oakland, California, have attempted to come to grips with these issues; however, more research to support objective project selection is required.

Achieving a better understanding of a cost of capital can be an important element in making appropriate allocation and financing decisions. For example, in many instances, priority is being given to projects with high levels of private sector participation. The long-term cost of these contributions may be substantially higher than comparable levels of public funding when the rates of return on invested capital are compared. However, the willingness of private investors to commit funds may be a useful indicator of a project with strong near-term benefits.

Private sector equity may require a 20 percent return on investment compared with an 8 percent municipal bond or a 7 percent Treasury bond. Determining which projects would be best funded from which sources and what the optimum mix of public and private resources should be for a given undertaking is necessary if the true costs of a project are to be understood and efficient allocation of capital is to be achieved. Similarly, providing for future capital replacement needs by recognizing depreciation in some manner could help decision makers select among projects, as well as make rational decisions regarding the scope of individual investments.

With proper planning and financial analysis tools in place, the following essential issues can be addressed:

- Can intermodal assessments be made to devise an optimum solution to a transportation need without regard to categorical funding biases?
- Can incentives be created to accept lower-cost alternatives?
- Can gains-sharing strategies be devised that permit underused services and facilities to be rationalized?

Research is also needed on techniques to minimize the human impacts of increased efficiencies arising from the introduction of new technology or more rigorous project selection criteria. Job displacement is a serious issue in retarding the introduction of new technologies and rationalizing existing services. For example, coordinated use of advanced computerized dispatching and vehicle locator and automatic fare collection systems could trigger significant changes in the delivery of transit services. Fixed route service built around 40-ft buses might be made obsolete in many areas.

New types of services employing information-based technologies noted previously could offer feasible alternatives to single-occupant automobile travel in areas of dispersed development at delivery costs much lower than those of conventional public transit. At the same time, the impacts on existing institutions and labor might be substantial and act to deter aggressive experimentation. It is essential that the paths to implementing new "soft" technologies with potential for cost savings and better service in popularly desired development patterns not be ignored in research initiatives that are purely hardware oriented.

Finally, it is important that technological research recognize the market reality that consumers prefer cars and living in single-family homes on large lots and recognize the land use implications that follow. Transportation finance could be greatly facilitated if taxpayers and consumers were offered a choice of products and services that enabled them to satisfy their life-style preferences.

CONCLUSION

In summary, the impacts of financing mechanisms on urban form are limited, compared with market and regulatory influences. The implications for land use tend to arise in a negative sense from inadequate public funding for transportation improvements. The greater the development pressures and the shortfall in improvements funded from broadly based revenue sources, the more significant will be the impacts of specific transportation mechanisms on urban form. Public-private partnerships have an important role to play in transportation finance; however, their significance as a funding source has been oversold in many cases and frequently arises as a solution only after the public sector has failed to perform. Adequate public dollars are almost always needed to connect spot improvements that may be financed through fees, proffers, and assessments.

Future research should be targeted at improving the ability to allocate limited capital resources rationally in a highly politicized environment, increasing the legitimacy of needs assessments at the project and regional level, removing institutional barriers to deriving the benefits from new technologies, and targeting technology development toward products and services that respond to actual lifestyle preferences.

REFERENCES

1. G. Giuliano. *Report 1—Literature Synthesis: Transportation and Urban Form.* School of Urban and Regional Planning, University of Southern California; FHWA, U.S. Department of Transportation, October 1989.
2. D. J. Forkenbrock, T. F. Pogue, N. S. J. Foster, and D. J. Finnegan. *Road Investment to Foster Local Economic Development 1.* University of Iowa Public Policy Center and Midwest Transportation Center, Iowa City, Iowa, May 1990.
3. J. R. Kenworthy and P. W. G. Newman. *Learning from the Best and the Worst: Transportation and Land Use Lessons from 32 International Cities with Implications for Gasoline Use and Emissions.* School of Environmental and Life Sciences, Murdoch University, Perth, Western Australia, October 1987.
4. C. B. Leinberger. Development Trends and Real Estate Opportunities in the 1990's. *Urban Land,* December 1990, p. 4.
5. W. Kulash, J. Anglin, and D. Marks. *Traditional Neighborhood Development—Will the Traffic Work?* ASCE, New York, N.Y., March 1990.
6. *Fact Sheets for Reauthorization Proposal for Surface Transportation.* FHWA, U.S. Department of Transportation, February 1991.
7. *Transit Fact Book.* American Public Transit Association, Washington, D.C., 1989, p. 24.
8. Transit Deficit has Tripled in 7 Weeks. *The New York Times.* February 21, 1990, p. B1.
9. *Zoning News,* American Planning Association, Chicago, Ill., December 1990, quoted in *Land Use Digest,* Urban Land Institute, Washington, D.C., January 1991, p. 2.
10. *Growth Management Studies Newsletter,* University of Florida, June 1990, in *Land Use Digest,* Urban Land Institute, Washington, D.C., January 1991, p. 2.
11. *Special Assessment Financing for Transit Improvements.* Joint Center for Urban Mobility Research, Rice Center; UMTA, U.S. Department of Transportation, July 1987.

Regional Governance of Metropolitan Form: The Missing Link in Relating Land Use and Transportation

DOUGLAS R. PORTER
Urban Land Institute, Washington, D.C.

Metropolitan areas in the United States are evolving within a framework of governance that is calculated to support and reinforce the most desired life-styles of Americans. Most residents (and voters) in the United States place a high value on living in a semirural environment and driving their cars to work, shopping, recreation, and every other aspect of their daily lives. The resulting urban sprawl and automobile dependency are endemic in the metropolitan regions of the United States. Unfortunately, this mode of living and traveling is expensive in terms of infrastructure requirements, environmental damage, and equitable service to all sectors of the population. Those costs appear to be increasingly unbearable both economically and politically.

The governance systems established to guide development of metropolitan areas, however, are intended to further those development objectives, or at least to avoid interference with them. States have given local governments powers to control the character of development and have structured tax policies that buttress the tendencies of local governments to pursue fiscal and exclusionary land use policies. In the transportation arena, states essentially have retained control over major highways, the backbone of metropolitan transportation systems, leaving feeder roads and transit systems mostly to local control.

63

These divisions of labor among state and local governments have failed to produce rational or systematic strategies for development of metropolitan areas, in which most Americans reside and work. To bridge that governance gap, the federal government in particular has encouraged the formation of regional or metropolitan agencies to provide information on growth trends, prepare long-range plans to meet future needs, and support implementation efforts.

After nearly three decades of experience, almost none of these agencies has proved successful in setting and meeting regionwide objectives for either land use or transportation. Most regional agencies are almost powerless to steer any other course than the status quo, and few are capable of determining or implementing metropolitan development strategies. With no one in charge, public guidance of metropolitan development is fragmentary, discontinuous, and ultimately ineffective.

Three working models of regional planning and implementation enlighten this bleak state of affairs. Perhaps the most successful of these models relates not to metropolitan development but to preservation of important natural resources, frequently those threatened by unguided metropolitan growth. Another model is the rare regional agency that possesses significant powers to implement urban growth strategies at the regional scale. Finally, the model offered by Florida's regional planning agencies suggests a potential if not fully realized solution. To adapt these models to effective metropolitan governance of land use and transportation, however, will require a broader vision of the future metropolis, an informed constituency that understands the shortsightedness of parochial decision making, and federal and state initiatives to define and empower regional decision making.

The discussion that follows will attempt to sort out how land use and transportation decisions are made, and how those processes and procedures may ultimately affect the form and character of metropolitan development. The focus is on highway transportation and transit, the systems most used by metropolitan residents. By tracking the decision paths that typically lead to land use and transportation decisions, the key points of interaction can be defined and their influence on metropolitan growth patterns can be discerned.

DOMINANCE OF THE MARKETPLACE

At the outset, it is perhaps useful to remind readers that public policies and public institutions tend to play supporting rather than principal roles in determining metropolitan growth patterns. Metropolitan development in the United States is driven by market forces that are only marginally influenced by public policies and regulations. This is so obvious a statement that public officials often forget that their efforts to plan and manage development more often guide than direct development choices. At the simplest level, most development occurs because the market demands it. The market indicates land use and transportation preferences, and public policy decisions usually are keyed to market choices—either stimulating, supporting, or dampening them. The regime of public decision making may modify the actions of the marketplace but only to a degree, and perhaps a fairly small degree.

Transportation systems, of course, offer public officials a powerful tool for influencing urban form and quality, especially in the urbanizing fringes of metropolitan areas where our future cities are being created. Not surprisingly, perhaps, public officials have voted to support the market with massive highway building programs, tempered to a degree by the transit system investments of the past decade or two.

And there is the nub of the problem. Downs has spoken and written extensively about the gap between the daily mode of living desired by most Americans and the mode that most city planners and traffic engineers believe is most appropriate (*1*). Americans generally want a house on a large lot and three cars in every garage, or rather on the highways (typified by the title of an article by Dubbink: I'll Have Mine Medium Rural, Please) (*2*). Yet that dream translates into low-density sprawl and dependence on roads and highways, a pattern of spreading metropolitan development that is expensive in terms of public and private infrastructure costs, quality of life, and environmental damage. A reality gap exists in this vision of life in America. Some people can afford to bridge the gap by spending more to support their expensive habits. But many people cannot, and many people are weary of long commutes and worried about the disappearing countryside. The maturing environmental movement is forcing a reexamination of the modus operandi of urban development. The high costs of infrastructure improvements also are encouraging a reevaluation of current land use. Perhaps the time has come for rethinking public decision making at the metropolitan level of governance.

PUBLIC GUIDANCE OF LAND USE

Zoning and subdivision controls adopted and administered by local governments compose the basic public decision arena for determining land use. Leading to this decision point are several levels of public determinations about urban development. They begin with official projections of population and employment that define land use demands for housing, retail, industrial, and other development. In most metropolitan areas these projections for local jurisdictions are subsets of regional projections, probably modified to some degree by local governments to reflect their particular version of reality. Projected demands and needs are then shaped by a set of local public policies to form a comprehensive plan or set of functional plans intended to portray the shape and content of future development. These ideas are extended into regulatory and programmatic actions that specify in greater detail what can or should be built and where. Ultimately, public entities act to approve individual developments, either by administrative action or by discretionary determinations after hearings and negotiations that often modify the private proposals and that may not reflect adopted policies.

Multiply this line of decisions by the number of separate jurisdictions in a given metropolitan area and it equals regional urban form—or does it? The metropolitan regions defined by the 1980 U.S. census contain an average of about 100 governments of one kind or another—counties, cities, towns or townships, school districts, and various other special purpose districts (3). But individual decisions by these many local governments reflect differing preferences for the living environment and often stake out competitive rather than shared positions. Such decisions usually create externalities that alter development parameters in other communities. Responses to those externalities occur at different times. So the sum of land use decisions by individual local governments rarely shapes up to a cohesive regional land use pattern.

This is the case particularly in rapidly growing cities, counties, and towns that are attempting to accommodate or stem the tide of development. Many of these jurisdictions have adopted the point of view that "less is more"—that reducing development densities, fending off projects that generate traffic, and encouraging up-scale construction will make their political and residential life more pleasant. Such communities tend to condition approvals of development projects on drastic reductions in proposed multifamily housing, increases in lot sizes, cutbacks in commercial retail development, and extensive reservations of open space. In practice, these individual decisions that generally reduce densities deflect urban growth into the countryside, virtually eliminating opportunities for transit service and excluding families that need moderate-cost housing.

At the metropolitan level, such practices encourage suburban and exurban sprawl, with consequent losses of open space, agricultural lands, and environmental resources and mounting requirements for expansions of infrastructure systems. Most metropolitan areas are experiencing a shortage of affordable housing located reasonably near employment centers. Most have grave difficulties siting locally undesirable land uses, which now include major highway corridors.

Waiting in the Wings: Regional Councils

Regional organizations exist in almost every metropolitan area to provide forums for coordinating the plans of local governments and in some cases to insist on meeting a certain standard of planning and implementation. Furthermore, in eight states, state governments also are watching over the machinations of local governments and providing state goals by which regional agencies can insist on more rational regulatory behavior by local governments. The National Association of Regional Councils counted 523 such regional organizations in 1985. Many of these serve primarily rural areas, but about 302 are based on metropolitan areas (4). Most are creations of states that carved out substate regions and encouraged or mandated formation of regional planning councils or agencies. Regional groups generally are organized as councils of local governments and act as regional service agencies for various functions such as economic development, environmental protection, and transportation planning.

Such regional organizations, unfortunately, are seldom effective in curbing the land use excesses of local governments or pursuing coordinated metropolitan growth strategies. Instead they provide data, services, and some planning:

• They often constitute the chief source of population and economic data and projections for regions and their component jurisdictions. Thus, by default they provide the parameters of future development planning for local governments. But local governments frequently argue over projections and modify them to meet their own needs. In the 1980s, also, regional projections frequently missed the mark.

• Regional agencies provide forums for reaching consensus among local governments about land use issues. Although such forums offer avenues for cooperation and coordination that otherwise do not exist, they often devolve into elaborate games of mutual backscratching rather than significant trade-offs among divergent interests.

- Regional agencies often provide clearinghouse functions or selected regionwide services of use to local governments. A few manage important infrastructure systems such as sewer and water or park systems. Many act as the designated agency for federal programs such as metropolitan transportation organizations, programs for the elderly, and job training.
- Regional agencies may prepare regional land use plans to coordinate local decision making, but many do not. A few states require regional agencies to adopt plans that coordinate local plans. Most do little more than stitch together local plans without proceeding to input any regional strategies.

What do these regional organizations accomplish "on the ground," so to speak?

- Most regional plans are only advisory. Because relatively few regional agencies can coerce local governments to respect regional plans, they have no incentives to adopt regionwide strategies that vary significantly from plans of individual local governments. Some regional agencies—perhaps many—lack staff to track local plans to see how decisions are consistent with regional plans and forecasts. Furthermore, regional planning based on collations of local plans of necessity lags behind local plan making and plan changing.
- Agencies that have powers to require local plans to conform to regional or state goals frequently avoid the hard choices, because they remain chiefly or totally controlled by and financially dependent on their constituent local governments.
- The jurisdictions of most regional agencies encompass areas either too large or too small for effective control of metropolitan growth. Many include vast rural areas that will not be urbanized for decades, thus diffusing their urban focus. Many metropolitan councils of government, on the other hand, adhere to U.S. census regions that fail to include major urbanizing fringe jurisdictions. By definition, the planning orientation of most such regional organizations is a decade behind the metropolitan development process.

These characteristics of regional agencies suggest that the network for land use decisions in most regions largely bypasses significant regional inputs. Four types of regional organizations, however, offer potential models for effective metropolitan management of land use: environmentally based organizations, urban-oriented agencies, metropolitan authorities, and agencies backed by state growth management legislation.

Regional organizations are able to mobilize support for regionwide strategic planning and action for issues considered serious enough and common enough to all jurisdictions to warrant special action. The principal issue that has merited that kind of attention is protection of special environmental features. Regional agencies set up to ensure protection of Lake Tahoe, the New Jersey Pinelands, the Columbia Gorge, the Chesapeake Bay, and similar natural treasures have been empowered to override local decision making and frequently do so. They are unusual, however, in having state and often federal charters that make them anomalies outside the general system of government.

Regional organizations that focus primarily on urban development issues rarely enjoy the types of powers given environmentally based agencies. The notable exceptions in Minneapolis–St. Paul, Minnesota, and Portland, Oregon, serve to point up the weaknesses of regional organizations in other metropolitan areas. The Portland and Twin City regional agencies possess substantial powers to influence local decision making on land use issues, including maintenance of urban growth boundaries and direct or collateral management of vital public service systems. Neither agency, however, comes close to being a "regional government," because they provide only selected services and depend for the most part on consensus building and cooperative relationships with local governments, rather than coercive regulations.

Another type of regional organization that can make a significant impact on local land use is the regional authority or commission. These exist in many metropolitan areas to provide specific services to all or part of the region. Examples are the New York Port Authority, the Washington (D.C.) Suburban Sanitary Commission, and the Metropolitan Parks and Open Space Commission in the Minneapolis–St. Paul area. The actions of these agencies can have important effects on local land use, and they often do. Many, however, are either formally or informally restricted from unilateral action in local jurisdictions, and their programs may not serve wider regional interests.

State Initiatives To Encourage Responsible Planning

New state legislation to manage growth suggests that states will increase their influence over local decisions on land use. In the past 5 years seven states (Florida, New Jersey, Vermont, Maine, Rhode

Island, Georgia, and Washington) have enacted growth management laws, and several more appear to be gearing up to pass new statutes. A close inspection of this trend in the making, however, indicates that only Oregon, Vermont, and Florida have established a track record in state growth management, and their experiences to date are quite different. Seventeen years ago Oregon adopted a law requiring all local governments to plan according to specified state goals and prompting those jurisdictions to plan at some level of competence. Furthermore, the state goals have led local governments to adopt urban/rural boundaries and encourage higher-density housing, both intended to prevent urban sprawl. The Oregon law made no provision for statewide planning or for regional planning, except in the Portland area.

Florida adopted many elements of the Oregon system but added some other bells and whistles, including requirements for regional plan making, regional coordination of local planning, and concurrency of infrastructure improvements with development approvals. A 1975 Florida law also required regional planning councils to review developments of regional impact. Thus, Florida regional agencies, potentially at least, have been given a fair amount of power, but it remains to be seen how they will wield it. To date, few of them have used their powers significantly to change the direction of local planning. As an example, the mayor and vice-mayor of two neighboring Florida cities concerned with downtown redevelopment might be thought to be interested in regional initiatives that might constrain sprawl and refocus development toward their cities. Instead, neither professed any knowledge of his regional organization's planning for the region—to them it was essentially irrelevant. Another indication is the fact that although all Florida regional agencies were given power to mediate land use conflicts of local governments, to date none has used that power (C. Siemon, unpublished data).

Vermont's Act 250 (5) set up regional citizen's review boards to approve developments of regional impact. The boards act almost entirely outside the planning mechanism, having no requirement to adhere to local plans and no ability to prepare regional plans. The new act, 200 (6), sets up regional planning agencies, but their power is somewhat equivocal and has just been reduced through amendments.

A missing element in this discussion of state planning legislation is state planning, which in a direct land use sense is almost invisible. Several of the recent state laws, including Florida's, have required state agencies to prepare strategic plans and coordinate them with each other's and with local plans. These efforts have yet to pay off in coordinated approaches to influencing local land use. Of course, individual departments have tremendous effects on local land use, such as health department rules for septic tanks. But states generally have no strategies to guide urban development. New Jersey is struggling to adopt a statewide land use plan, and may yet. With no legislated implementation strategy, its potential effects on development are unknown. On the other hand, New Jersey's fair-share housing laws, stimulated by Mt. Laurel decisions and responsible in part for state planning actions, are having some effect on where and how affordable housing is built in New Jersey.

An essential component of the land use game is federal and state environmental regulation. In their administration of environmental laws, environmental agencies have increasingly restricted the use of environmentally sensitive lands for urban development, backed up by many interest groups ready to enforce their demands in court. Again, these agencies and constituencies tend to be single-issue oriented, to be reactive to specific development proposals, and to lack a strategy for metropolitan land use and development.

Except in a few areas, therefore, most public decisions on land use still occur at the local level, guided only marginally by regional concerns. At the metropolitan level, decisions are weakly coordinated, discontinuous, incremental, and unsystematic. Most decisions are driven by consumers and voters who desire low-density development with a high degree of automobile mobility.

PUBLIC GOVERNANCE OF TRANSPORTATION SYSTEMS

Compared with the governance of land use, decision making for transportation systems is a model of clarity and rationality. Or is it? Starting at the level where public officials make commitments to transportation improvements, three types of decision making structures can be discerned, each of which takes place within different frameworks of governance. One is local governmental decisions in annual budgets to finance and construct local improvements—new roads, road widenings, traffic signals, contributions to transit systems, and so forth. The second is the local government's decision to shift some or all of these costs to developers through exactions or impact fees. The third is the state government's decision, usually after being prodded by local governments and developers, to fund transportation improvements manifest in annual budgets of state highway departments.

Many local governments undertake transportation improvements according to a 6-year capital improvements program (CIP), revised each year. The CIP schedule supposedly is based on analyses of needs, facility and system planning coordinated with land use planning, cost estimates, and projections of potential revenues to pay for improvements. The CIP is changed each year to reflect new needs, conform to budget realities—often shortfalls—and respond to "political sensitivities." The last may include pressures from neighborhood groups and influential developers to block or reschedule improvements or requirements to shift priorities because of decreased or increased development. The consequence in virtually all jurisdictions is that the programs are only rough indicators of actual improvements. In fact, it appears that most such programs never keep pace with needs, much less fund improvements according to a rational schedule.

CIPs have another flaw: major improvements, especially those involving state or federal funding, are usually keyed to regional transportation plans developed by metropolitan planning organizations and to annual state programs of improvements. As will be seen later, these plans and programs may not reflect actual needs at the local level.

The second means of funding improvements is through developer exactions and impact fees. Ostensibly the improvements obtained through these means correspond to local, regional, and state plans for timing and design, but the process is skewed by the fact that developers are contributing cash, land, or facility construction. Such contributions often are treated essentially as "off-budget" funds, not subject to the same scheduling considerations as publicly funded improvements. In fact, the current favorite device for accomplishing much-needed construction in the face of funding shortages is to "allow" developers to "advance" local and state schedules of improvements. Developers whose projects fail adequate facilities tests are given the choice of either delaying their projects until the public schedule finally rolls around or funding improvements themselves.

This means that developers, if they can afford it, can call the shots on when improvements are made and often how they are made. They may negotiate understandings on improvement designs, phasing, and even location. These negotiations are not necessarily wrong (and may even instill more realism into decisions about construction needs and timing, especially if verified through development agreements) but tend to undermine the credibility of official programs.

The third process is a state's decision to fund particular highway or transit improvements. And here the focus should be on the metropolitan planning organizations (MPOs), which since 1962 have been responsible for determining needs and priorities for metropolitan transportation improvements funded by state and federal funds. The famous "3C" mandate enacted in 1965 called for continuing, comprehensive, and cooperative planning for transportation, which in turn required the formation of metropolitan agencies that could coordinate state and local actions (7). Because this corresponded with the period of founding regional land use planning agencies, the two types of agencies were often combined. But MPOs are different from land use agencies in important ways. MPOs have boards usually appointed by governors and are closely affiliated with state transportation agencies, rather than beholden to local elected leaders. Therein lies the strength—and weakness—of MPOs. They are capable of looking beyond local concerns to deal with metropolitan needs and priorities, but much of what they do must pass muster with local governments that are not well integrated into the system.

MPOs have not proved to be as successful at coordination and cooperation as everyone had hoped. As with regional planning agencies, typically they have no implementing powers. They plan and program transportation improvements but are at the mercy of other state and local agencies to carry out plans. The state plays a mercurial role in the MPO planning and programming process. Because the MPO exists mostly to assure rational allocations of federal and state funding for transportation improvements, it would seem to have a lot of power. And MPOs' annual adoption of multiyear transportation improvement programs (TIPs) promises an orderly and thoughtful procedure for determining priorities for funding improvements. Such is seldom the case. State departments of transportation still carry the most influence in highway funding. If state officials suddenly want to switch project priorities or add or drop projects from the current year's program, the MPO's transportation improvement program can be and frequently is modified to reflect those changes. In other words, TIPs are just as vulnerable as local CIPs to political and other maneuvers. Furthermore, because federal regulations in 1982 allowed states to formulate and monitor their own programs, states are free to structure procedures that leave their hands untied by metropolitan agencies.

MPOs' records with local governments are also problematic. In the Washington, D.C., area, transportation planners trot out the tale of the "Incredible Shrinking Plan" as one explanation for traffic congestion. The comprehensive transportation plan carefully crafted in the 1960s to serve future traffic needs was amended time and again as various jurisdictions refused to retain important segments of planned highways in their plans. Whole expressway corridors were dropped, as were innumerable feeder arterials. Now the plan cannot serve the needs of the existing population, much less the future one (8). That story has been played out in countless metropolitan areas. In addition, most MPOs are subject to local governments' ideas on land use, a problem discussed in the following section.

So MPOs are center stage for highlighting regional needs and meshing transportation with land use objectives, but are hobbled by the same problems as regional land use planning agencies. Left unsaid is that both types of agencies are drastically underfunded for accomplishing even their basic missions.

KEY INTERACTION POINTS IN LAND USE–TRANSPORTATION DECISION MAKING

If the governmental decision making processes for land use and transportation systems are compared, three key points can be discerned at which coordinated action would contribute to effective metropolitan strategies for land use and transportation:

1. The reflection of regional forecasts of land use and transportation trends in local strategies for land use and transportation;
2. The synthesis or reconciliation of local plans in regional plans; and
3. The response of local governments to gaps and conflicts defined in the regional planning process.

Tailored Forecasts

One of the key opportunities for coordinating local with regional development strategies concerns the periodic demographic and economic projections usually generated by regional agencies. Many regional agencies possess enough competence to employ complex computer models for regional projections and allocations to local areas. At the metropolitan scale, such projections are reasonably accurate and supply a useful accounting framework for projecting small-area trends in local jurisdictions, traffic zones, and so forth. MPOs usually base their traffic projections on such forecasts, and local governments rely on such projections for their planning of land use and transportation patterns. The forecasts thus provide an important mechanism for coordinating local with regional planning.

As is often the case, this straightforward model of intergovernmental behavior breaks down in practice. Three problems have emerged. First, at the local level, a variety of local cities, towns, and counties are intent on deciding their futures individually. They may, on their own initiative, use regional demographic and economic forecasts prepared by regional agencies, and may reflect regional transportation plans based on those forecasts in their own plans. Or they may, and often do, choose to modify regional forecasts and plans to suit their own ends, especially as the benchmarks of the decennial census fade in time. In addition, local governments may discount or resist use of periodic updates of long-term forecasts by regional agencies if the projections suggest the need for unwanted policy changes.

A second and perhaps more fundamental problem is that regional allocations of demographic and employment projections to individual jurisdictions are based on the adopted plans of local jurisdictions. Indeed, in many regions the initial round of inputs for projections is furnished by local planners who derive their numbers from official plans and zoning. These sources, however, may reflect exclusionary attitudes or desires to emphasize particular types of development regardless of market realities or may simply be obsolete. Nevertheless, if West Podunk plans and zones large acreages for 2-acre lots, the projections will reflect that policy position. If, on the other hand, East Podunk decides to become a powerhouse employment area by reserving a quarter of the town for industrial purposes, that goal, too, must be recognized in the forecasts. Although such plans are modified to some extent when used in forecasting models—which usually control projections within regional and area totals—regional numbers must to some extent reflect local policies on land use, thus disciplining the projections in sometimes surreal ways.

Central cities, for example, frequently protest projections that show stable or declining growth in population and employment. A recent check with MPOs in the Denver and Miami areas illustrates the point: elected officials in both cities routinely insist that projections indicate substantial growth for their cities, despite steady losses in residents and jobs over many years. Transportation planners in Denver coped with suburban Aurora's plan for seven regional shopping centers in a 7-square-mile area by instructing their model to eliminate one in every five centers. These accommodations to fit forecasts to local policies appear to be quite common.

The third problem is that local officials undoubtedly peg their visions of land use futures on their sense of likely transportation improvements, thus creating a chicken-and-egg situation. Local plans seldom evolve from a zero base on a clean playing field. Local officials have been playing the land use and transportation game for years; past plans and actions have set the parameters of probable futures. Absent bold proposals or major policy shifts by regional or state agencies, why should local governments assume that radical new strategies are possible or probable? Thus, local plans are likely to be based on assumptions that past land use and transportation interactions and patterns will be maintained.

These problems mean that land use and transportation strategies become caught in a policy loop that protects the status quo. Local government planning for land use and transportation inevitably is based on projections already reflecting presumptions about future development strategies. Furthermore, to the extent that local objectives do not match regional projections, local governments are quite willing to "take down" allocations of expected growth different from those that regional agencies propose to allocate to them. Except in a few areas, local governments are not enjoined to accept fair share allocations of regional projections. Thus, the potential discipline that regional forecasts might provide to guide local plan making is frequently flouted.

Reconciling Regional and Local Plans

The second key transaction point involves the synthesis of local plans with regional land use and transportation plans. Through this process, regional agencies have an opportunity to introduce regional visions of metropolitan development, which in turn may provide a framework for local plans and a means of meshing land use and transportation objectives and intentions. Regional agencies also can point up conflicts between regional and local objectives and take steps to reconcile differences.

Unfortunately, in most metropolitan areas this approach to assuring that regionwide development strategies are addressed falls prey to the governance gap. Although MPOs are required to prepare regional transportation plans, other regional planning agencies often have no mission to draw up regional land use plans. Lacking that, they often fall back on assembling local plans, tailoring the rough edges to make them fit but otherwise accepting local expectations for future development. Even if regional agencies prepare plans that represent regional interests, they generally have no way to impose regional priorities on local plans. MPOs, through the implementing actions of state transportation departments, may have some influence over local transportation planning, but most regional development plans have only advisory status. As an illustration, the recent massive planning effort carried out by the Puget Sound Council of Governments was based on urban development extending only to Lake Sammamish, but hardly before the ink was dry on the plan, a new 5,000-acre mixed use development was approved east of the lake. Thus, local governments are rarely called on to abide by regional plans, much less consider regional priorities. Even in those states that have state-mandated regional and local planning requirements, regional agencies have limited powers to engage in effective strategic planning.

Failures in Feedback

The third key point at which local and regional interaction might afford opportunities for consideration of regional interests is in feedback of regional forecasting and planning exercises to local governments. Apparently, however, most regional planning agencies do a poor job of reporting back to local governments the implications of such analyses for local plans, and an even poorer job of encouraging local governments to amend their plans to reconcile conflicts. The process works to accept and mold local plans to the requirements of regional forecasting and allocation models, but little information filters back to local governments. Models employed by the Puget Sound and Metro Dade agencies, for instance, internally balance land use allocations among jurisdictions and small areas, but the ways in which such changes match up with local plans are never determined. Seldom are MPOs able to suggest to local governments that their land use policies result in unworkable transportation systems and should therefore be revised.

On the basis of evidence from several regional agencies, such intergovernmental communication is short-circuited in many cases by staff shortages at both regional and local levels. On a purely informational basis, those local governments with professional staffs usually manage to keep up some interchange of information about regional activities, but too many small suburban and rural communities are understaffed for such purposes. When staff members at the Denver Council of Governments, for example, tell local planners about revisions in planned land uses that are made in the course of running the traffic forecast model, they are greeted with blank stares and shrugs.

The key point here is that local governments can choose to ignore regional plans with impunity, and frequently never learn about the plans of neighboring jurisdictions until too late to negotiate compromises or head off bad decisions.

TOWARD EFFECTIVE METROPOLITAN GOVERNANCE

What metropolitan areas need and seldom have are regional agencies capable of looking out for the metropolitan good, agencies that can raise the planning horizon from individual corridor studies and project approvals to thinking about the future development of the region as a whole, including how land use development should correspond with transportation system improvements. Such regional agencies would then possess the conceptual base for evaluating local plans against regional objectives and for calling attention to regional prerogatives.

To accomplish this end, such organizations should have both the mission and budget to formulate workable regional plans, should have some powers to influence funding allocations and implementing regulations throughout the region, and should be capable of overriding decisions of individual local governments on critical issues. At a minimum, such agencies should be responsible for determining the conformance of local plans with regional plans and reporting inconsistencies to local governments. Although regional organizations need not—and probably should not—possess comprehensive powers for planning and managing growth and development, experience with the present ineffectual systems indicates that they must have some administrative and funding capabilities to influence the actions of local governments.

How can such a model of regional governance be achieved? Four directions of research might elicit useful answers to that question.

Forming a Metropolitan Vision

Before great strides can be taken toward effective strategies for metropolitan development, a new vision of the metropolitan region as the living space most Americans inhabit must be formed. The vision must be as persuasive to metropolitan citizens as the dream of rural landscapes and living styles has been to generations of Americans. Analytic explorations of the metropolis as a network of nurturing environments for living, working, and enjoying recreational activities would encourage planners of future urban areas to consider ways to weave land use and transportation systems together. The vision would encompass concepts of living and working spaces mutually related to transportation and other infrastructure systems and to natural preserves that provide breathing room for urban residents. The governance role of regional institutions would evolve from this new understanding of metropolitan futures.

Defining a Metropolitan Constituency

A constituency of concerned citizens would be fundamental to work toward the vision of the future metropolis, much as the environmental movement has galvanized action on environmental issues at all levels of society. The urban quality of life that could be realized in metropolitan regions can be pictured as a genus endangered by current shortcomings in regional governance. The status quo in metropolitan development threatens everyone's quality of life, a fact that can be underscored by descriptions of major issues, such as traffic and waste disposal, poorly addressed by our present system of regional nonplanning. We need to define closely the many interests affected by such problems, including business and consumer groups, who might support more effective metropolitan management of land use and transportation development.

Improving the Data Base on Regional Models

The various models of regional governance existing today provide a rich source of information that has largely been untapped. These models should be evaluated for their effectiveness under a variety of circumstances. Whether state backed or locally subscribed, such organizations should be analyzed to determine the critical functions they may provide and the roles they might be empowered to play. Such analyses should also seek better information on the interplay of land use and transportation relationships in metropolitan growth and development—the principal substantive concern of regional governance.

Defining New Programmatic and Regulatory Techniques

Regional actions to determine and effectuate related land use and transportation futures will only come from federal and state initiatives to support such actions. Alternative program and regulatory initiatives at federal and state levels should be examined. Should transportation agencies, for example, require demonstrations of the linkage of proposed transportation improvements to supportive and responsible land use goals? Or should urban mobility be subject to a "no net loss" policy similar to the current federal wetlands policy? Could transportation agencies express a clear preference for local governments that coordinate their plans with regional goals? Should state transportation agencies formulate state policies for supporting metropolitan development? If so, what types of policies might be considered? How might federal and state agencies leverage local requirements for making development contingent on "adequate facilities"? What funding support, even taxing powers, might regional agencies acquire to provide them means for effective leadership in metropolitan growth and development?

In conclusion, it bears repeating that the institutional framework created for decision making in land use and transportation issues succeeds in the objectives set for it: avoiding intrusion into local decision making and perpetuating the status quo. Somehow, the widening reality gap must be bridged with workable, regionwide institutions of governance.

ACKNOWLEDGMENT

The author wishes to thank Robert Dunphy, Director of Transportation Research at the Urban Land Institute, and his research associate, Kim Fisher, for their mini-survey of metropolitan planning organizations and helpful information on the origin and operations of such organizations.

REFERENCES

1. A. Downs. *The Need For a New Vision for the Development of Large U.S. Metropolitan Areas.* Salomon Brothers, New York, August 1989.
2. D. Dubbink. I'll Have Mine Medium Rural, Please. *Journal of the American Planning Association,* Autumn 1984.
3. *The Practice of State and Regional Planning* (F. S. So, I. Hand, and B. D. McDowell, eds.). American Planning Association, Chicago, Ill., 1986, p. 133.
4. *Directory of Regional Councils, 85–86.* National Association of Regional Councils, Washington, D.C., 1986.
5. Vermont Environmental Board. Act 250, Title 10, Chapter 151, 1970.
6. Vermont Department of Housing and Community Affairs. Act 200, Title 24, Chapter 117, Effective July 1, 1988.
7. Federal Aid Highway Act of 1962. PL 87-866, October 3, 1962.
8. G. V. Wickstrom. Forecasts of Anticipated Travel Demand for the Washington Area. *The 1990s and Beyond: Critical Choices for the Washington Metropolitan Region.* Proceedings of a Regional Conference on Growth and Transportation, Metropolitan Washington Council of Governments and the Transportation Planning Board, Washington, D.C., 1989.

Energy and Environmental Research Needs

DAVID G. BURWELL, KEITH BARTHOLOMEW,
AND DEBORAH GORDON
Rails-to-Trails Conservancy, Washington, D.C.;
One Thousand Friends of Oregon, Portland, Oregon;
Union of Concerned Scientists, Washington, D.C.

A High Priority National Program Area (HPNPA) is being developed by FHWA for research on the efficiency of future national transportation systems. This research will be conducted over 5 years and will target highway system planning and management in congested urban areas and development of data systems and analytical methods for use in financial planning, highway system planning, and environmental and economic analyses.

The research will focus primarily on solutions to urban congestion, the abundant use of oil, and air quality problems (*1*, pp. 7, 9).[1] The research agenda will look at a common component of these problems: the interaction between land use and transportation. The contributions of land use and urban form to the pressing transportation problems of congestion, energy use, and air quality are not well known. The goal of this research program is to identify short-term and longer-term strategies to reduce congestion, energy use, and air pollution by strengthening the connection between land use planning and transportation.

This paper draws on the resource papers, background literature, workshop reports, and discussion from this conference and on outside research to identify a potential research agenda in the area of energy and the environment. The objective is to understand how the urban transportation-land use planning and decision making process could be improved to achieve national energy efficiency and environmental objectives while meeting urban mobility needs.

81

One bias must be disclosed at the outset. This conference identified a significant gap in adequate data bases and models for research. In some cases transportation planners are using models based on demographic data collected in the 1960s. Two types of data needs were identified:

1. Baseline data on demographics, mode choice, travel characteristics, and so forth that can be used in new travel forecasting models and

2. Behavioral data that analyze how specific measures taken to promote a public policy objective succeed or fail in achieving that objective.

Research focusing on problem-solving and evaluation rather than on developing new simulation models that have no particular ability to inform public policy decisions is favored in this paper. Research to inform decision making in five areas involving the construction and use of national transportation infrastructure is particularly timely. These areas are as follows:

1. **Trip generation decisions:** These are decisions made by individuals about where to live and work, whether to make a trip, and what mode to use. The presumption is that information on the energy and environmental costs of such decisions, if made known to transportation consumers and charged back to them at marginal cost, would influence their behavior.

2. **Investment decisions:** These are decisions made by responsible elected officials and transportation professionals to invest in particular transportation solutions. The presumption is that information on the effects of such decisions on transportation demand, energy, and environment and on total environmental and energy costs would affect these decisions.

3. **Finance decisions:** These are decisions made by federal, state, and local officials on how to assess the costs and benefits of transportation services and improvements among various users. They include decisions to tax, toll, or subsidize certain transportation-related services and address how these decisions affect energy efficiency and the environment.

4. **Land use–planning decisions:** These are decisions made by local and regional officials (mostly elected but some agency officials) on whether and how to regulate certain land uses based on the ability of existing and potential future transportation capacity to serve those uses and the energy and environmental consequences of such decisions.

5. **Project decisions:** These are decisions made by land developers to proceed with land development projects on the presumption of availability of sufficient transportation infrastructure to support such projects and the energy and environmental consequences of such decisions.

Almost all of the research needs relating to energy and environmental issues identified at this conference and discussed in the workshop reports seek to inform one or more of these five types of decision making. By dividing energy and environmental issues among these various types of decision making it is hoped that the research protocols developed for environment and energy issues as a result of this conference will place great emphasis on the ability of research results to inform real-world decision making. By making the connection between research and decision making, this new FHWA High Priority Program will significantly strengthen the linkages between transportation, urban form, and the environment.

PROBLEM STATEMENT

A healthy transportation system is vital to national well-being, no less than a healthy circulatory system is vital to personal well-being. A strong, balanced, and interconnected system of rail, highway, transit, air, water, bicycle, and pedestrian facilities supports a strong, balanced, and efficient domestic economy while also improving the ability to compete in international markets. The national interest clearly is served through the development and maintenance of a sustainable program for the delivery of transportation services that strengthens national and international competitiveness, maintains national security, promotes the achievement of national clean air goals, enhances energy efficiency, and improves the overall quality of life.

Unfortunately, transportation is also a heavy consumer of natural resources, particularly land and energy, and can also degrade air quality.

Land

Low-density development increases transportation energy demand, air pollution, vehicle miles traveled (VMT), and natural resource consumption (2–4). For example, the California State Highway Division calculates that single-family residences on 1/2-acre lots generate 12.5 car trips per day, whereas such development on 1/8-acre lots generates 8.5 car trips per day (2–4). Nevertheless, land densities are declining (5, p. 2). For example, in the Chesapeake Bay area, the average developed acreage per capita in 1950 was 0.18, but had increased to 0.65 by 1980. This means that average densities declined from more than five people per developed acre to fewer than two (5, p. 2). Within urbanized areas, both residences and work places are dispersing from the classical concentric configuration to sprawling low-density development (6, p. 2). Despite sprawl, length of work trips is decreasing (2, Table 10, p. 32). The percentage of all work trips that were less than 6 miles increased from 52.2 percent in 1969 to 54.1 percent in 1983 (2, Table 10, p. 32). Work trips account for less than 25 percent of local automobile trips in urbanized areas and less than 30 percent of total VMT (6, p. 2). However, work trips contribute disproportionately to energy and environmental costs because of their concentration in peak travel periods and the fact that they are characterized by very low occupancy ratios: 1.15 people per car compared with 1.7 for the average car on the road (7, p. 20).

Energy

Per capita gasoline consumption in U.S. cities is nearly 4.5 times higher than in European cities and 10 times higher than in Japan. Despite new car fuel efficiency gains, automobile travel consumes 40 percent more oil now than 15 years ago. Approximately 68 percent of all vehicle trips operate on the urban driving cycle (less than 30 mph average) (8). Fuel consumption doubles when speed drops from 30 mph to 10 mph (9). Transportation accounts for more than 63 percent of total domestic oil consumption, most of it to fuel private automobiles. If energy costs to build infrastructure, produce fuel, and manufacture vehicles are included, transportation accounts for 72 percent of total domestic oil consumption (10). Today half of U.S. oil is imported; by 2010 the U.S. Department of Energy projects that oil imports will amount to 70 percent of demand, mostly for transportation (11).

Air Quality

Motor vehicles account for 25 percent of all U.S. emissions of CO_2, a primary greenhouse gas, and 16 percent of U.S. emissions of chlorofluorocarbon, another greenhouse gas and a primary destroyer of the ozone layer, and they indirectly contribute to buildup of methane and tropospheric ozone through emissions of nitrous oxides and CO (1, pp. 7–9). (Tropospheric ozone and methane also contribute to the greenhouse effect.) Increases in VMT have overwhelmed progress in reducing tailpipe emissions: 27 additional cities violated national ambient air quality standards (NAAQS) for ozone in 1988. More than 100 cities now violate ozone standards; 44 violate CO standards (*12*, p. 6). (Transportation sources account for approximately two-thirds of U.S. CO emissions.) Congestion exacerbates air pollution problems, yet VMT is projected to increase 45 percent by the year 2010, whereas highway capacity will only increase 6 percent.

Urban areas bear the brunt of these problems, yet the interest in clean air, energy security, and natural resource protection elevates these problems to a national level. Solutions to these problems will require unprecedented cooperation at all levels of government as well as technological improvements and efficient pricing of transportation services to change personal transportation habits.

CREATING A DECISION-BASED RESEARCH AGENDA

Research, to be useful, must inform decision making. High-priority areas for research, broken down by decision making area, include trip generation decisions, investment decisions, finance decisions, planning–land use regulation decisions, and project decisions.

Trip Generation Decisions

Obviously, the decision that has the greatest ability to minimize transportation-related energy consumption and pollution and to reduce congestion is the decision of whether and how best to make the trip. (In one of the workshops at this conference, it was discussed whether, if a car was invented that emitted no pollution and consumed no fossil fuels, there would still be concern about urban form. The consensus was yes, because of other problems, such as congestion, land consumption from sprawl, infrastructure costs, etc.) What research is needed to inform individual decisions on these two important questions? Changes in consumer behavior are predicated on choice. If consumers have no choice in the process of trip selection, no behavior changes are possible. Therefore, research focused on strategies to reduce the energy and environmental impacts of urban form must focus on how to provide a sufficient range of energy-efficient and nonpolluting transportation choices, given a consumer's mobility needs. Options include the following.

Total Internalized Trip Cost

What are the total costs of particular types of trips (e.g., commuting, recreation, shopping) by vehicle occupancy and trip length? New models are needed to include not only the marginal and fixed costs by mode but also costs for lost productivity paid in time spent in congestion. All costs paid by the user (e.g., in dollars, time, and equipment maintenance) should be included in this calculation.

Total Externalized Trip Cost

What are the total societal costs of these same trips? A new system of accounts is needed to include deferred maintenance of existing transportation infrastructure as well as costs in pollution, energy waste, health, and so forth. The presumption is that if individuals knew the true cost to society of their trip and modal choices, such knowledge would influence their behavior even if they were not individually charged for such costs.

Allocation Mechanisms

Research is needed on methods to allocate the societal costs of mobility to those responsible for the costs (7, p. 41). (One researcher puts these externalized costs at $260 billion per year, or about $2.53 for every gallon of fuel consumed.) The presumption is that if all true costs were charged back to the user, fewer energy-intensive and highly polluting trips would be taken.

Telecommuting

Telecommuting has not achieved the results hoped for 10 years ago in reducing VMT, pollution, and energy consumption by reducing the need to travel. Why not? Is telecommuting simply shifting travel to different times of day? Is telecommuting a potentially effective transportation demand management (TDM) strategy? What additional information or service needs do consumers need to make it work?

Land Use and Trip Generation

What land use patterns are most efficient in serving total mobility needs? What densities and development characteristics support which modes? Household characteristics, as well as a simple measure of units per acre, must be considered, given the vastly changed household demographics in the past 20 years (i.e., reduction in persons per household). What types of mixed uses minimize travel demand? Case studies of communities such as Davis, California; Portland, Oregon; and Boulder, Colorado, may be helpful (*13*). Is single-use zoning a mistake because of its heavy demand on transportation services? What are some successes and some failures of single-use and mixed-use zoning? What are the salient factors to consider?

Reducing Discretionary Travel

Between 1969 and 1983 commuting declined from 33.6 percent to 30.1 percent of household VMT, whereas discretionary VMT (shopping and personal business trips) increased from 19.3 percent to 30.4 percent of household VMT (*14*, p. 3; *15*). What accounts for this significant growth in discretionary VMT and what role do transportation–land use interactions play in this growth?[2] Do any data later than those for 1983 exist?

Investment Decisions

The people who decide how a region is to grow are the people who decide land use and transportation. Unfortunately, the same people do not always make both types of decisions. Land use decisions are made by local elected officials and zoning boards or, in locations without any land use regulation, by private developers. Transportation investment decisions, particularly for large capital projects requiring federal or state assistance, are made by regional or state bodies and agencies. Often the decisions of these regional and state agencies are influenced more by the laws and regulations under which they operate (which regulate the amount of available dollars for transportation investment and the manner in which they can be disbursed) than local needs. The result is a mismatch between transportation and land use decision making that results in inefficient and polluting transportation–land use networks.

The lack of connection between transportation and land use decision making has become more pronounced as federal laws mandating improvement in urban air quality are strengthened. Research is needed to allow a fuller understanding of the nature of the potential conflicts among transportation, air quality, and land use planning and of how federal and state transportation polices and programs can exacerbate or resolve these conflicts.   Possible legal and regulatory solutions must also be reviewed.   Some appropriate areas of research are discussed below.

Update The Costs of Sprawl

In 1974 the U.S. Council on Environmental Quality published a book entitled *The Costs of Sprawl (16),* concluding that automobile-related pollution would be reduced significantly in planned developments and that the economic and environmental costs of high-density development were significantly lower than those of low-density development.   Significant methodological deficiencies have been identified in this study.   A new baseline study is needed to inform regional and statewide transportation and planning officials of strategies to integrate transportation, land use, and clean air planning.   In particular, research is needed on (a) how land use decisions drive transportation demand; (b) how transportation investment decisions drive land use decisions; (c) how geographic information systems (GIS) technology could be used to integrate transportation, land use, and air quality planning, particularly in the development of long-range transportation plans; and (d) the costs to the public of uncoordinated transportation, land use, and clean air planning.

Study Growth Management

Policy options available for public action to manage growth and link land use decisions to capital transportation investment decisions are becoming more numerous.   Studies are needed of state and local growth management plans and ordinances in Oregon; Washington; Maine; Rhode Island; Vermont; New Jersey; Georgia; Montgomery County, Maryland; and Florida, as well as trip reduction ordinances (TROs) in the South Coast Air Quality Management District of California and elsewhere (*17, 18*).[3]   Specifically, how successful have these laws and ordinances been in shifting transportation investment decisions to favor more energy-efficient and more pollution-free solutions?

Perform Needs Assessment

At this conference it was generally agreed that planning and investing in transportation projects to achieve a certain level of service (LOS) is no longer an adequate criterion to serve regional needs. Although LOS is a measure of relative congestion, certain areas actually plan for a low LOS as "traffic calming" measures to protect neighborhoods, reduce VMT, increase pedestrian activity, and promote clean air. In other areas, where improvements to traffic flow are clearly needed, the expansion of roadways to improve LOS may not be feasible. If LOS is not the measure for assessing transportation need, what is? What mediating structures exist to reach political consensus on a transportation mission at the metropolitan planning organization (MPO) level and on strategies to promote that mission?

Measure Air Quality Improvements

The Clean Air Act Amendments of 1990 place significant new constraints on transportation projects in nonattainment areas to actively promote the achievement of NAAQS (*19, 20*).[4] Yet few data exist to measure the ability of any specific transportation project to promote clean air goals by achieving specific mobile source emission targets. Research is needed to assist MPOs in measuring the ability of specific types of TDM and transportation system management (TSM) strategies and new transportation investments to meet real, quantifiable NAAQS targets.

Integrate Planning with Funding

Regardless of how well transportation, land use, and air quality planning is conducted at the MPO level, often federal and state transportation funding restrictions override good planning and direct funds to projects inconsistent with regional goals. Research is needed on how to bring planning and funding decisions together to achieve regional air quality and energy efficiency goals.

Apply Least Cost Planning

Efforts to manage demand and to provide for new demand through "least cost" methods have met with significant success in the electric utility industry. However, the decision making structure is much less fragmented in the utility industry (most electricity is generated from large central generating facilities). Also, there is relative uniformity between sources of electricity, whereas transportation is differentiated by mode (e.g., bicycle versus car), by quality of experience (e.g., Volkswagen versus Cadillac), and by trip length (e.g., a 5-mile trip may provide several modal choices, but a 20-mile trip may provide only one modal choice). Is it possible to apply the "least cost" planning model to the transportation sector while accommodating individual choice by mode, experience, and trip length (21)?[5]

Study Retrofitting

How do transportation investment alternatives vary in relation to the state of urban development? Are different models needed depending on whether population is growing, stable, or shrinking? Do alternatives vary depending on whether decision makers are trying to change the form of a built, mature city or trying to control future growth of a young city?

Finance Decisions

Both pricing and financing of transportation projects have a dramatic effect on what gets built and maintained. Who benefits? Who pays? These are two important questions with significant consequences in mode selection, land use patterns, and investment decisions. Research items that emerged at this conference are discussed below.

Fiscal Zoning

As bedroom communities grew up around major cities over the past 30 years, suburban officials were hard pressed to provide water, sewers, roads, schools, fire protection, and other services for these communities. The result was the adoption of favorable zoning laws to attract the retail and commercial base needed to support (in sales and property taxes and assessments) the cost of municipal services. This drained older cities of their commercial base and encouraged urban sprawl. Research is needed to understand this problem and to evaluate alternative solutions, such as tax-base sharing, to reduce energy-intensive and highway-intensive land use patterns. (Ironically, according to one conference participant, the land use that generates the greatest total public revenue is the strip-zoned automobile mart consisting of automobile dealerships and automobile repair services.)

Private Financing

The decline of general revenue sources in relation to growing travel demand is increasing pressure to assess the cost of transportation improvements on private developers in the form of fees, assessments, and proffers. Private funding for transportation improvements is totally disconnected from planning, because planning is designed only to guide the investment of public transportation dollars. Research is needed to assess the threat private financing poses to land use planning and to design solutions that promote energy efficiency and air quality.

Parking

More than 75 percent of all employee parking is provided free. Employers can deduct the full cost of providing employees with free parking from taxes, although the same employer can deduct only $15 per month for providing employees with free transit passes. Of course, parking is not free; costs are simply shifted from the user to the public in reduced tax revenues and higher infrastructure costs. Research is needed on the public costs of employer-provided free parking, not only in dollars but in energy use, land use, and pollution. Alternative parking management strategies and parking limitations to reduce home-to-work car commuting should be investigated. One strategy that deserves special investigation is the South Coast Air Quality Management District plan to have employers pay a commute allowance to all employees and then charge an equivalent amount for parking.

Gas Tax/Carbon Tax

The United States has the lowest gas tax of any industrialized country, the highest absolute number of registered motor vehicles (185 million), and the highest number of vehicles per licensed driver (1.03) and accounts for fully 50 percent of the world's VMT. Yet VMT is growing at a rate of 3 to 6 percent per year in most urban areas, far outpacing the ability of the transportation infrastructure to accommodate such growth. Research is needed on the connection between energy price and vehicle use. How important is energy price to modal choice? What is the price elasticity of transportation energy demand? At what price do alternative fuels become economically feasible? What is the range of public policy options at the federal, state, and local levels to use fuel pricing to achieve public policy objectives in coordination with transportation and land use planning?

Mortgage Interest

The home mortgage interest deduction has dramatically increased demand for single-family homes, thus greatly influencing land use patterns and, consequently, demand for transportation services. Reduction or elimination of this tax benefit is unlikely in the foreseeable future. However, research on the connection between this public policy, land use, and transportation demand is needed.

Land Taxes

Many transportation improvements are promoted not to meet existing demand but to serve new development. Private financing of these projects is one strategy for imposing the costs of such improvements on the developers who primarily benefit from these projects. (A project that has received national attention as a model for private financing of a major highway improvement is the Dulles Access Road Extension in Loudon County, Virginia.) Alternative strategies for capturing the value of transportation improvements are needed. Levying a special capital gains tax to capture the increase in land values resulting from transportation improvements may be a way of financing future transportation while keeping the planning and funding decisions within the public sector and connected to regional energy and environmental goals. This strategy has been adopted with apparent success in Europe. Research is needed comparing the European model with the private financing model in relation to regional energy, environmental, and land use objectives.

Price Goods Movement at Marginal Cost

Approximately 50 percent of urban transportation is for the movement of goods, not people.[6] Research is needed on how to charge back to freight haulers the marginal cost (both economic and social) of their use of urban transportation systems.

Planning and Land Use Regulation

Land use and transportation planning converge at the regional level. New governmental structures, such as regional zoning authorities and special transportation districts, are being formed to allow elected officials to address the problems of transportation, urban form, and the environment at the regional level. These new agencies and strategies hold some hope for the promotion of regional air quality and energy efficiency goals. Research needed to inform decision making at this level includes the following topics.

Urban Boundaries

Land use planning designed to fight "hopscotching" and isolated development and to direct urban growth inward can have dramatic effects on regional VMT growth and transportation energy demand while improving mobility (*22*). An ordinance designed for just this purpose has been enacted in Portland, Oregon. A case study of the "urban boundary" concept is needed as well as an analysis of its ability to promote energy efficiency and air quality.

Demand Management

Much research has already been conducted on TDM and TROs (*17, 18*). However, more research is needed to identify both alternative institutional arrangements needed to ensure adoption and implementation of these measures and the policy instruments needed to encourage these arrangements to develop (*14*, pp. 8, 9).[7] TDM and TRO measures alone will not work; they must be backed up with policies, programs, interagency agreements (memorandums of understanding), reporting structures, support structures, economic incentives, and possible sanctions. A compendium of such policies and a survey of such institutional arrangements are needed. In particular, policies that establish substantive TDM or TRO objectives should researched, such as the following:

1. **VMT growth caps:** Ottawa, Canada, and Boulder, Colorado, have set absolute VMT growth caps in their long-range transportation plans. How extensive is this practice throughout the nation?
2. **Parking caps:** Caps on parking spaces as a ratio of retail floor space are one option. Other parking limitation equations should be studied as well for their ability to reduce VMT and encourage mode shifts.

Congestion Management

Smart highways, high-occupancy-vehicle lanes, flow improvements such as reversible lanes, and other TSM improvements are all possible strategies to increase highway capacity and reduce congestion in the short term. However, little is known about the effect of such strategies on urban land use and total travel demand in the long term. There is some evidence that such strategies, if not coordinated with land use planning, simply encourage users to take longer trips, thus increasing total VMT, pollution, and energy use. Research comparing the relative ability of TSM and TDM strategies to achieve regional energy, environmental, and land use objectives is needed.

Corridor Preservation

Transportation planning traditionally accommodates future transportation growth based on a static land use plan. No attempt is made to influence future land use patterns to channel future transportation demand toward underused transportation corridors, such as abandoned rail corridors, and to encourage the preservation of such corridors for future transportation uses. Research is needed on ways to integrate transportation and land use planning to make maximum use of the existing transportation infrastructure to serve future transportation needs and on strategies to preserve abandoned railroad corridors and other transportation infrastructure for future transportation use.

Methodological Issues

Most transportation modeling programs (e.g., EMME2) do not integrate land use policy changes over time into projections of future transportation demand, distribution, or traffic flow. Alternative methodologies are needed that integrate land use and TDM strategies as dynamic variables in the modeling process. Specifically, methodologies are needed to allow analysis of alternative land uses in the alternatives analysis section of project-level and plan-level environmental impact statements (EISs).[8]

Methodologies are also needed using GIS and computer-aided mapping to integrate air quality, transportation, and land use planning.[9]

No federal, state, or local standards of performance exist for transportation energy efficiency. Methodologies should be developed to establish such standards (e.g., BTU per passenger mile), as well as mechanisms for measuring and enforcing such standards over time.

Air quality models for future transportation systems at the long-range plan level do not integrate the effect of subsequent transportation improvements occurring between plan creation and construction and tend to ignore land use decisions in the region they are likely to affect. Yet the Clean Air Act Amendments of 1990 require transportation planning to demonstrate absolute progress toward achievement of NAAQS over time. Transportation and air quality modeling must be integrated to assure absolute progress toward achievement of NAAQS as the plan is implemented.

The ITE *Trip Generation Manual* (23) does not take TDM strategies, such as parking price and availability, into consideration in its traffic forecasting models. This results in inflated traffic forecasts that are then used to justify projects that may not have been required if TDM and TSM strategies were adopted. A major overhaul of the *Trip Generation Manual* (23) is needed, as is research in support of an improved manual.

Modal Split

Rather than planning to achieve a particular LOS within a region, how feasible is it to model the energy and environmental impacts of alternative modal splits at a given level of total transportation use (mobility?) in the future? For example, Boulder, Colorado, has adopted a plan to achieve zero VMT growth and a 15 percent bicycle share of the modal split for peak commuting period by the year 2000. How extensive are such standards in transportation planning and goal-setting? What variables most affect modal split? Can they be quantified and incorporated in alternative regional transportation plan models?

Project Decisions

Decisions by public decision makers to invest public funds in transportation infrastructure were addressed in the section entitled Finance Decisions. This section addresses research needs to influence private decision makers, primarily developers, in deciding where to develop, how to provide adequate transportation services to the development, and how to design the development to minimize energy and environmental impacts. Some salient research items include

• How should land use be configured in developing areas to reduce travel demand?

• How big a barrier are zoning and subdivision ordinances and street design criteria to the integration of park and ride facilities, paratransit, bicycles, and buses into project designs? For example, do minimum turning ratios for fire engines in subdivision ordinances eliminate the possibility of bicycle lanes or sidewalks? How can these local requirements be adjusted to encourage a maximum range of modal choices?

• What are appropriate site development standards to address pedestrian, bicycle, and transit availability? What potential exists to encourage these alternative transportation modes through such standards? Where are the modal standards? How successful have they been in achieving their objectives?

• Is there an ideal size for shopping malls to achieve energy efficiency as a VMT generator?

The city of Davis, California, puts an 8-acre limit on new shopping malls. What is the basis for this limitation? What effect does it have on the secondary energy and environmental impacts of mall development?

CONCLUSION

The research agenda for transportation, urban form, and the environment could be expanded indefinitely. However, the problems of urban congestion, air pollution, global warming, and energy security must be addressed now. This conference and the research agenda being developed by the FHWA High Priority Planning Program are a welcome initiative to all who are interested in the energy and environmental impacts of the present transportation infrastructure.

The focus of the research agenda on urban areas and, in particular, on the role of urban form (land use) in advancing or defeating national energy and environmental objectives is extremely timely. The experience of the 20 years since the Clean Air Act was enacted in 1970 demonstrates that tailpipe emission controls and stationary source controls alone will not achieve NAAQS. Mobile source controls that focus on the need to use the private automobile and that provide transportation consumers with choice among modes must be addressed. Such choices cannot be developed fully without integrating urban form and land use considerations into transportation and air quality planning.

Energy considerations are also increasing in importance as the percentage of total domestic oil consumption derived from imported oil creeps over 50 percent. Transportation accounts for fully 63 percent of total domestic oil consumption directly as fuel and 72 percent of total domestic oil consumption, if the cost of refining and transporting fuel and the energy cost of building and maintaining our transportation infrastructure are taken into account. Essentially all (97 percent) transportation fuels are petroleum-based. Global warming is a direct result of the burning of fossil fuels, primarily oil and coal. Indeed, questions of national energy security and global warming cannot be dealt with if transportation is not addressed.

This research agenda is a welcome start in the attempt to integrate transportation, land use, and air quality planning to promote national energy and environmental interests. It comes not a moment too soon, and will receive the full support of the national conservation and environmental community.

NOTES

1. Although the HPNPA focuses on air quality and urban traffic congestion as driving the need for research on ensuring the efficiency of future transportation systems, it is likely that global warming will become an increasingly important force in focusing future transportation research on demand reduction strategies and the transportation/land use connection. Motor vehicles currently account for 25 percent of total U.S. carbon dioxide (CO_2) emissions and 67 percent of total U.S. carbon monoxide (CO) emissions (*1*, pp. 7, 9).
2. Michael Replogle has done some work in this area (M. Replogle, unpublished data). Preliminary data indicate that more home-to-work trips are linked trips (e.g., shopping, dropping children off at day-care) as well as the work commute. Statistically, these are discretionary trips but actually they are work trips. The growth in linked trips increases automobile dependency because they involve several destinations. Mixed-use land patterns that allow more pedestrian solutions to these trips (e.g., dropping children off at day-care close to home on the way to the bus) should be researched as a means of reducing automobile dependency.
3. FHWA published a *Status of Traffic Mitigation Ordinances (17)* and an *Evaluation of Travel Demand Measures to Reduce Congestion (18)*, but these studies do not link specific strategies to the achievement of specific air quality standards or reductions in congestion levels. More research on measurable results is needed.
4. In the Clean Air Act Amendments (*19*), for the first time Congress established substantive air quality objectives for transportation plans and linked federal funding for transportation projects to the adoption of regional transportation plans containing quantitative mobile source emission targets. Under previous U.S. Department of Transportation interpretation of Clean Air Act and Federal Highway Act "conformity" rules, transportation projects had only to demonstrate that they did not actively prohibit implementation of transportation control measures (*19, 20*).
5. Of course, "least cost" means least *total* cost, including social and environmental costs. One of the greatest difficulties in applying this principle to transportation is the difficulty encountered in quantifying these costs and comparing them with total benefits. The challenge of such a methodology was clearly laid out by McHarg (*21*, p. 32):

> The objective of an improved (transportation planning) method should be to incorporate resource values, social values, and aesthetic values in addition to the normal criteria of physiographic, traffic and engineering consideration. In short, the method should reveal the highway alignment having the maximum social benefit and the minimum

social cost. This poses difficult problems. It is clear that new considerations must be interjected into the cost-benefit equation and that
many of these are considered non-price factors. Yet the present
method of highway cost-benefit analysis merely allocates approxi-
mate money values to convenience, a commodity as difficult to quantify
as either health or beauty.

McHarg wrote this at the time of the enactment of the National Environmental
Policy Act (NEPA), which attempted to inform decision making in just this
fashion. The relative inability of NEPA to apply the least total cost concept
to transportation decision making has led to renewed interest in this concept.
The Natural Resources Defense Council and the Conservation Law Foundation of New England have conducted research on application of the least cost
principle to transportation planning.

6. This figure comes from Workshop No. 2 (Wickstrom) and is attributed to Ken
   Ogden of the University of California, Irvine.
7. This research recommendation comes from Hillsman and Southworth (*14*,
   p. 9). They point out that what is understood about individual transportation demand involves mode choice rather than the decision or need to travel.
   Research focusing on the travel decision itself is a high priority (*14*, p. 8).
8. Proposals contained in the administration's Surface Transportation Act
   Reauthorization would delegate EIS responsibilities to states for the Federal
   Aid Urban and Rural Programs (a combined program in the proposal). Guidance on integrating land use and transportation planning in EIS documents
   should be a top priority if such proposals are adopted, because few states will
   have any experience in this area.
9. Although the use of GIS in transportation and land use modeling is in its
   infancy, some good work has been done (M. Replogle, unpublished data).

REFERENCES

1. J. J. MacKenzie and M. Walsh. *Driving Forces: Motor Vehicle Trends and
   Their Implications for Global Warming, Energy Strategies, and Transportation Planning.* World Resources Institute, Washington, D.C., December 1990.
2. P. Newman and J. Kenworthy. *Cities and Automobile Dependence.* Gower
   Publishing, Brookfield, Vt., 1989, pp. 34–68.
3. M. Renner. *Rethinking the Role of the Automobile.* Worldwatch Paper 84.
   Worldwatch Institute, Washington, D.C., 1988, pp. 35–45.
4. D. Gordon. *Steering a New Course: Transportation, Energy, and the Environment.* Union of Concerned Scientists, Cambridge, Mass., 1991, pp. 57–67.
5. *Managing Growth in the Chesapeake Region: A Policy Perspective.* Alliance
   for the Chesapeake Bay, May 1989.
6. I. S. Lowry. Planning for Urban Sprawl. In *Special Report 220: A Look Ahead:
   Year 2020,* TRB, National Research Council, Washington, D.C., 1988.
7. D. Gordon. *Steering a New Course: Transportation, Energy and the Environment.* Union of Concerned Scientists, Washington, D.C., 1991.
8. F. Westbrook and P. Patterson. Changing Driving Patterns and Their Effect on
   Fuel Economy. Presented at the 1989 SAE Government/Industry Meeting,
   Washington, D.C., May 2, 1989.

9. California Energy Commission. *Transportation Issues—1990 Conservation Report.* Public hearing document, May 1–2, 1990.

10. S. Casler and B. Hannon. Readjustment Potentials in Industry Energy Efficiency and Structure. *Journal of Environmental Economics and Management,* Vol. 17, pp. 93–108.

11. *U.S. Department of Energy Posture Statement and FY 1992 Budget Overview.* Report DOE/CR-0002. U. S. Deprtment of Energy, Washington, D.C., February 1991, p. 5.

12. *National Air Quality and Emissions Trends Report.* U.S. Environmental Protection Agency, Washington, D.C., March 1989.

13. T. Oppenheimer. Creative Alternatives to Urban Sprawl: A Tale of Two Cities. *Utne Reader,* May/June 1989, pp. 95–98.

14. E. L. Hillsman and F. Southworth. Factors That May Influence Responses of the U.S. Transportation Sector to Policies for Reducing Greenhouse Gas Emissions. In *Transportation Research Record 1267,* TRB, National Research Council, Washington, D.C., 1990, p. 3.

15. *The FHWA/Faucett VMT Forecasting Model.* Report JACK-FAU-88-336. Jack Faucett Associates, Bethesda, Md., 1988.

16. *The Costs of Sprawl.* Council on Environmental Quality; Real Estate Research Corporation, Washington, D.C., April 1974.

17. *Status of Traffic Mitigation Ordinances.* Report DOT-T-90-06. FHWA, U.S. Department of Transportation, August 1989.

18. *Evaluation of Travel Demand Measures to Reduce Congestion.* Report FHWA-SA-90-005. FHWA, U.S. Department of Transportation, February 1990.

19. Clean Air Act Amendments of 1990, amended Section 176(c). PL 101–549, November 15, 1990.

20. Procedures for Conformance of Transportation Plans, Programs, and Projects with Clean Air Act Implementation Plans. Memorandum of Understanding between U.S. Environmental Protection Agency and U.S. Department of Transportation, June 12, 1980.

21. I. L. McHarg. *Design with Nature.* Conservation Foundation Washington, D.C., 1969.

22. M. Replogle. Computer Transportation Models for Land Use Regulation and Master Planning in Montgomery County, Maryland. In *Transportation Research Record 1262,* TRB, National Research Council, Washington, D.C., 1990, pp. 91–100.

23. *Trip Generation Manual.* ITE, Washington, D.C., 1976.

Research Needs for Analyzing the Impacts of Transportation Options on Urban Form and the Environment

DANIEL BRAND
Charles River Associates, Inc., Boston, Massachusetts

Aparadigm is introduced that demonstrates the difficulty of promoting land use patterns that reduce travel in metropolitan areas. The paper also describes the increasing costs of urban congestion because of individuals who make travel decisions without confronting the full costs of their individual choice behavior. These costs cannot be avoided in today's complex economic system, and manifest themselves as reductions in the quality of life and in the value of massive private investments in real estate. The paper provides a taxonomy of transportation options organized around the production of more information to travelers on the actual costs of their travel in real time, information satisfying final demands, as well as capacity increases to help ensure the efficiency of future urban transportation systems. A list of research needs is developed to help the U.S. Department of Transportation develop a research agenda for analyzing transportation options in terms of their full range of impacts on urban form and their environmental and other external or social costs that individuals do not internalize and account for in their travel decisions. The research needs follow closely the topics and paradigms developed in the paper.

101

BASIC UNDERSTANDINGS AND BACKGROUND

Interaction Between Transportation and Urban Form

A paradigm shift is needed in the way the interaction between transportation and urban form is viewed. In heartfelt planning goal statements this interaction continues to be viewed in terms of an incomplete model of travel and land use location behavior. This occurs when the hopeful question, Are there land use patterns that reduce urban travel? keeps being asked. This question has not been answered in the affirmative on a metropolitan-wide scale because the relationship is not directly causal. There is a third variable driving them both, namely, the behavior of individuals that affects the demand both for land use and travel.

The question, Are there land use patterns that reduce travel? exemplifies the prevailing "partial equilibrium" model of travel demand. In this model, travel, whether predicted with the Urban Transportation Planning System (UTPS) or a "direct demand" model, is considered to be conditional upon a fixed land use pattern. Land use patterns, of course, are not fixed. It would be desirable to have the research and planning budgets to develop long-run "general equilibrium" models that would enable the prediction of land use and travel simultaneously (1) as these are determined by a given transportation system and by the many other determining factors so eloquently stated in other papers at this conference.

The suggested new paradigm for how the interaction between transportation and land use is viewed is shown in Figure 1. It is based on the behavior of individuals, the bad guys to whom Schulz referred in his keynote address to this conference—incorrigible in their habits, but generally predictably so. Quoting Schulz:

> I believe that those of us concerned with transportation in urban America can no longer wait for people to start to behave as we'd like them to: living in compact, high-density residential development patterns; traveling short distances to work along well-defined corridors to destinations in orderly, compact business districts; using public transit in large numbers because they want to, not because they have to; planning their nonwork travel in orderly and efficient ways; and being very socially conscious in their selection and very limited personal use of an automobile. We have to recognize the reality that people are very unlikely to accept, and are in fact likely to strongly resist, significant changes of this sort, especially if they perceive that such changes are limiting their personal freedom of choice.

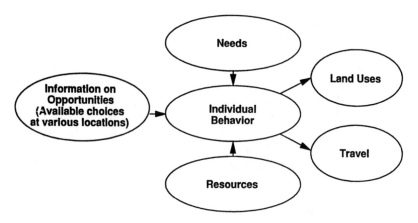

FIGURE 1 Suggested paradigm for land use–travel interaction.

Referring to the paradigm in Figure 1, the individual to whom Schulz refers has information about a set of opportunities to engage in activities at various locations, some or all of which may involve travel. The individual also has needs—to work, shop, play, be safe, and have a home. These clearly condition how the individual chooses among various activity opportunities involving travel. The individual also has resources (e.g., time and money) that affect response to opportunities to travel and location of activities at various places and prices.

The lack of a direct causal relationship between land use and travel is shown in Figure 1. As mentioned earlier, there is a third variable driving them both, namely individuals responding to opportunities, needs, and resources to "consume" both land and travel. Empirically, the presence of the third variable has been amply demonstrated, causing individuals to consume both more land and more travel as their income increases. In her paper at this conference, Deakin states, "If, as is usually the case, transportation is cheap relative to housing and one can buy more house per dollar farther from the center, households will have an incentive to live farther away from their workplaces."

For better or worse, major investments in highways in the 1950s and 1960s, successful in enabling increased labor productivity and economic development, have sown some of the seeds of their own failure, as is so often the case in an economic system as complex as that of the United States. Success in increasing real incomes in society through transportation and other economic investments has resulted in increased demand for housing to improve the standard of living. The well-known result of this is that higher real incomes lead urban populations to move farther out from the city centers because more housing can be consumed on more land, as well as more travel at a lower total cost. Until now, the added utility of cheaper land, housing, and a pleasant environment farther from the city centers has been greater for the more affluent urban population than the added disutility of the transportation cost of traveling to and from dispersed housing, employment, shopping, and so forth.

The paradigm in Figure 1 shows that any attempt to reduce travel involves influencing individuals to reduce their consumption of both land and transportation. New high-density developments with possible associated lower travel requirements may appeal to a portion of the urban population, but will they change the overall travel requirements of the metropolitan-wide marketplace?

The paradigm in Figure 1 also suggests that efforts to promote higher-density developments may be appealing only to a relatively small segment of the market that prefers high-density development and walking or traveling short distances to work. This may be only one tail of the distribution of individual behavior as it reveals its preference for housing and employment locations. It may be a mistake to think that an entire distribution of individual behavior can be changed by catering to particular market niches. Indeed, high-density developments must not be made so difficult for travelers that they are not marketable at all.

Finally, the paradigm in Figure 1 suggests that additional measures costing real money are needed to promote certain land uses as an effective way to reduce total vehicle or person trips in urban areas. One type of measure would hit the individual in the pocketbook as a means of inducing him or her to live and travel at lower total social costs. This means internalizing some costs that are not now paid by the individual. Alternatively, taxpayers would pay to provide socially efficient housing and employment choices at lower than private market costs. Absent these stick-and-carrot approaches, simply requiring new developments to be designed to reduce travel may not change the overall distribution of individual behavior in a way that reduces total travel.

Costs of Congestion

Until recently, the transportation cost of adopting and maintaining an affluent land use and transportation-consuming suburban life-style was low. Fuel was, and remains, relatively cheap, and the fuel taxes levied to build and maintain the transportation infrastructure are only about 10 percent of the total internalized cost of the national automobile-truck-highway-transit system. Fuel taxes are presumed to be an even lower percentage of the total social cost of the transportation system.

But the era of cheap transportation may be coming to an end. As real income has been increased through real labor productivity increases over the last few decades in the United States, a life-style has developed that involves consuming increasing amounts of transportation. Thirty-three percent more trips per person were taken in 1983 than in 1969 (*2,* p. 2). Preliminary results from the 1990 Nationwide Personal Transportation Study data indicate that trip lengths in urban areas that had remained relatively constant in miles between 1969 and 1983 appear to have increased by 10 to 15 percent over their 1970 to 1980 levels (*3*). In addition, large metropolitan areas now contain many more people. Ninety percent of the entire population growth of the United States in the last decade (1980 to 1990) occurred in metropolitan areas of more than 1 million people. For the first time, a majority of Americans (50.2 percent) now live in these large metropolitan areas, compared with 45.9 percent in 1980 (*4*).

It has been said that congestion is the price we pay for free movement. Unfortunately, the free ride may be coming to an end. The capacity of highways in metropolitan areas is quite finite. As the organizers of this conference have stated, current post-Interstate planning "shows a rather grim outlook for highway performance in our major metropolitan areas over the next several decades."

The automobile-highway system is a classic example of a system that puts private interests over the public interest and is characterized by individual choice. Every time a person drives his or her car onto a congested roadway, far more aggregate delay is imposed on others—on the system—than on the driver. This aggregate delay on others results, in turn, in far more air pollution and energy consumption by others than by the individual causing the delay and pollution in the first place. In economic terms, the marginal private cost of highway travel is much lower than the marginal social cost of travel on the already congested highway system. In fact, the more congested the highway corridor, the greater the difference between the marginal social and marginal private costs of making a trip by automobile.

This result is shown in Figure 2. V_0, where the demand curve and the marginal private cost curve intersect, represents the use of the highway under the present circumstances, where the automobile

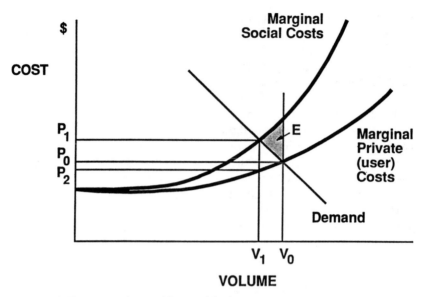

FIGURE 2 The congestion problem and its impacts.

user pays only the private costs of travel. The societally "efficient" amount of highway use, V_1, is at the intersection of the marginal social cost curve and the demand curve. The shaded area E, the difference between the marginal social cost curve and the current demand curve, represents the total loss to society from the individual's not perceiving and paying the full societal resource cost of a trip.

This loss to society, or "efficiency" loss, can be explained as follows. If the price of a good were to be less than the marginal cost of producing it, then it would be efficient to produce less of the good. Prices below marginal costs indicate that people are not willing to pay enough for the good to justify what the economy has to sacrifice (the marginal cost) to produce the good. If less were produced, then the value people give up by not consuming the good would be less than the value of the resources saved by not producing the good, and economic efficiency would increase if production were curtailed.

In order to examine options for maintaining urban mobility in the future that will ensure the efficiency of future urban transportation systems, consideration must be given to the congestion costs, which are the delays imposed on others when the individual does not pay the total resource cost of travel. These, in turn, contribute to the other components of the total social costs of added travel included in Figure 2.

Impacts on Land Use

Congestion is the price the system imposes as a result of individual private decisions to locate in sprawling regions and on larger plots of land, farther away from work and shopping. And as increasing amounts of money are spent on housing, the transportation price that individual life-style decisions impose on everyone else is not known by the individual when he or she makes those decisions. Investments are made by individuals in expensive housing without consideration of the total cost of their location decisions. This leads to real inefficiencies; the system has lost its ability to confront consumers with the real costs of their decisions. This is as true in the long run for land use location decisions that generate congestion as it is in the short run for individual travel decisions.

Cheap transportation enabled adoption of a suburban life-style, but transportation is no longer cheap. Congestion is becoming such a problem in metropolitan areas that it leads to a sense of disconnection and threatens the value of the recent massive increase in private investment in suburban and exurban housing and land. In the 1940s, 20 percent of income, on average, was devoted to housing. In the 1980s, this percentage rose to 40 percent (5, p. 202).

In the past 40 years, a life-style has evolved that involves spending much more, in both relative and absolute terms, on land and housing in the suburbs. Investing in real estate—individual home ownership—has been a very good investment. How long can this good fortune be expected to continue?

Meanwhile, public expenditures on highways have been cut in half as a percent of the gross national product since 1960 (6, p. 481). Much more private money is being spent on housing and much less public money on transportation. How long can this disparity in spending be expected to continue without destroying the value of real estate?

At the same time, congestion has increased to the point at which it is out of control, because individuals perceive only a fraction of the total congestion they cause. The capacity of the transportation infrastructure has not been increased to lower the levels of congestion (this would bring the marginal private and social cost curves in Figure 2 closer together), nor is it politically feasible to do so in many major cities. Adding capacity would at least have the effect of internalizing a larger fraction of the costs of travel decisions. In addition, there are so many more people in metropolitan areas that the demand curve in Figure 2 is shifting to the right, and the private and social costs of travel and location decisions are increasing and diverging.

In summary, transportation is no longer so cheap relative to housing. Referring to Figure 1, the cost of the combined land use-travel consumption package is increasing in a way that threatens to reduce the value of housing investments and the amenities of a suburban life-style. As in so many other sectors of a free market society, there is no free lunch. The axiom is "You pay now, or you pay later." The social and environmental costs of congestion are not being paid now by individuals when they make their decisions to consume land and travel (Figure1). If the urban transportation congestion problem is not addressed systematically with the options presented in the next section, we will pay later, as housing values and quality of life diminish with increasing congestion.

OPTIONS

This paper examines options for maintaining urban mobility in the future that will ensure the efficiency of future urban transportation systems. In doing this, a much larger variety of transportation options is available than was a decade ago. The incrementalism of the 1980s—"make no large plans"—seems to be at an end. Many of the options now involve new technologies and communications and may sound futuristic to some. Although it is hoped that they will be available soon, the time horizon for influencing urban form in coordination with transportation plans is also long.

The old saying "If we don't know where we're going, all roads lead there" could not be more true in this context. It is necessary to take a long view in regard to time and technology development to ensure success in this exciting undertaking.

Classes of Options

Figure 3 shows seven classes of options for providing future mobility, with an emphasis on land use–transportation coordination. These are

1. Providing up-to-date information to travelers on their real costs of travel,
2. Providing up-to-date information to transportation providers and institutions on the performance of their systems,
3. Providing conventional highway and transit system capacity increases,

4. Providing technology improvements that offer higher speeds and closer vehicle spacings,

5. Pricing transportation facilities en route and at trip ends,

6. Creating telecommunications options that can satisfy final demands (economic and social activities) where they require less or no travel, and

7. Creating regulatory actions and/or economic incentives that reduce the travel requirements of new or existing land uses.

Each of these classes of options holds considerable promise for helping ensure the efficiency of future urban transportation systems.

Travel Information

Without adding capacity, advanced traveler information systems (ATIS) can allow people to make informed choices to avoid congestion. The adjustments they make can involve changes in travel routes, mode, and destination or a decision to make the trip at a different time or not at all. These new traveler information systems will change the nature of the demand for travel by enabling travelers to know in advance and to control the levels of congestion at which they will travel individually. Ultimately, these traveler information systems may have a long-run dimension, forecasting travel conditions not only a half-hour in the future for short-run travel choices but also 5 years into the future for land use and activity location decisions.

Figure 1 suggests that such systems may have a profound effect on both land and travel consumption in metropolitan regions. Opportunities for activity at various locations are only as relevant as the information available about them and about the conditions of travel to reach those locations. This means that new traveler information systems will provide benefits as a result of the information they give to travelers on their expected trip times and costs, in addition to the benefits they give from shortening trip times. Simple technological calculations of increases in capacity with intelligent transportation systems will not provide a good description of the benefits. The benefits from such systems will come as much or more from user interactions with the system as from increases in effective network capacity supplied through short-term operational improvements to these systems. Nevertheless, the latter will certainly be an important result of an improved transportation information environment. Indeed, they are the second class of options that it is necessary to consider, as shown in Figure 3.

OPTION	DIRECT IMPACT			
	DEMAND		SYSTEM PERFORMANCE	
	SHORT-RUN TRAVEL	LONG-RUN ACTIVITY LOCATION	SHORT-RUN MANAGEMENT	LONG-RUN RESTRUCTURING
INFORMATION				
1. TO USER	X	X		
2. TO SYSTEM			X	X
CHANGING LEVEL OF SERVICE				
3. CONVENTIONAL TECHNOLOGY: INCREASE CAPACITY			X	X
4. NEW TECHNOLOGY: INCREASE SPEED/CAPACITY				X
5. PRICING			X	
TRAVEL SUBSTITUTION				
6. THROUGH TELECOMMUNICATIONS	X	X		
7. THROUGH REGULATION AND ECONOMIC INCENTIVES	X	X		

FIGURE 3 A taxonomy of options.

Information for Managing System Operation

The short-term system operational improvements that result from improved information on system performance and travel behavior will greatly benefit public and private transportation providers in their ability to manage the available system capacity in real time. Advanced traffic control systems will be able to respond more intelligently and make more efficient use of available highway network capacity. They will even be able to change the modes of transportation options offered [e.g., by setting up high-occupancy-vehicle (HOV) and transit options as warranted by conditions such as major accidents and other incidents that cause the majority of traffic delays].

Capacity Increases

New construction decisions to increase the capacity of current transportation modes will also be made with much more information about their effectiveness. Many needed improvements in the current highway and transit systems have been backlogged by a shortage of money for construction and maintenance. As shown in Figure 3, the most direct impact of this third class of options will be in terms of the long-run restructuring of the physical transportation system. The new transportation information environment will allow the pinpointing of recurrent bottlenecks causing congestion and accidents and enable the most cost-effective capacity increases to accommodate travel to be made, regardless of mode. There is also considerable interaction between Options 2 and 3, because the capacity increases can provide more flexibility for appropriate short-term system management responses to unusual traffic conditions.

New Technology

New technology will not only allow the more efficient construction and operation of conventional modes, it will also provide the fourth set of options in Figure 3, involving higher speeds and closer vehicle spacings. High-speed trains are already operating in Europe and Japan but not in the United States. Introducing higher speeds at the metropolitan scale may have dramatic effects on urban form— even to the extent of tying nearby metropolitan areas together (e.g., Baltimore and Washington). Automatic vehicle control (AVC) systems would provide much closer vehicle spacings and possibly higher speeds that would dramatically increase system capacity. Elements of AVC systems show considerable promise of being introduced in the 1990s to improve automobile driving safety (e.g., vehicle proximity and lane-edge warning devices).

Providing higher ground speeds and capacities is perhaps the easiest of the new technologies to evaluate for impacts on demand and urban form and on congestion and other externalities. In contrast to the uncertainty of evaluating the impacts of improved information, the impacts of this fourth set of options are related to how they change conventional level-of-service measures (travel speeds, times, etc.).

Pricing

Some forms of pricing clearly are noncoercive, such as establishing new toll roads at market prices for congestion relief or providing incentives for HOV use (e.g., reduced HOV parking costs). Some forms of pricing may be more controversial, such as building new toll roads with public subsidies and charging vehicles using these roads by their weight, energy efficiency, or air pollution. This would allow pricing at levels that cover some or all of the social costs of driving on these new roads. Also controversial are proposals to tax the free parking employee benefit—or at least make employer transit subsidies tax free. These could help high-density central business districts. Some forms of pricing, such as areawide congestion pricing, are very controversial at the present time. Inevitably, however, pricing will be made much more possible, and very likely much more acceptable, as better information from new transportation technologies provides users and managers with informed choices on using transportation capacity more efficiently while still preserving people's freedom to travel when and where they want.

Telecommunications and Regulation

Ease of analysis does not characterize the sixth and seventh options presented in Figure 3. These are "travel substitution" options that involve changing the location of activities and reducing or even eliminating the travel required to carry out those activities. These options include

- Telecommunication that can satisfy final demands (work, shopping, and recreation activities) at locations requiring little or no travel and
- Trip reduction regulations such as HOV use requirements at employment sites to reduce vehicle trips or requirements for balancing jobs and housing and other housing or employment preference programs to reduce the person-trip requirements of new or existing land uses. These regulations also include more conventional restrictions on parking or on truck loading and unloading at curbs in city centers.

The first of these two options holds out the possibility of intervening in the paradigm in Figure 1 and reversing the positive but spurious correlation between the consumption of land and travel. To the extent that communications can satisfy final demands—economic and social activities at locations requiring less travel—there will be a reduction in the derived demand for travel.

On the other hand, the paradigm in Figure 1 suggests that additional measures costing real money are needed to make the seventh option an effective way to reduce total vehicle or person trips in urban areas. For example, if the costs of high-density developments can be lowered to compete with the lower costs of suburban housing, all else being equal, their cost advantage may help reduce travel. Alternatively, all taxpayers would pay to provide socially efficient housing and employment choices at lower than private market costs. Research on these issues is necessary, as proposed later in this paper.

Option Shifts

This discussion of options shows that there has also been a dramatic shift from 10 years ago in the options that transportation planners can consider to ensure the efficiency of future urban transportation systems. The incrementalism of the 1980s has given way to excitement in the field and many new possibilities.

The reasons for this shift are many. The problems are worse. As noted earlier, 90 percent of the entire population growth of the United States in the last decade (1980–1990) occurred in metropolitan areas of more than 1 million people. Congestion has grown with this population shift and with 10 years of economic boom in the 1980s, resulting in the marginal social cost of added highway travel rising much faster than its marginal private cost. It has also become very difficult to add new transportation capacity on new rights-of-way in most of our largest cities to alleviate this congestion. At the same time, the components of the social cost of congestion—delays imposed on others, air pollution, energy consumption, and housing and income distribution disparities—are moving much higher on the social agenda.

Solutions to these urban transportation problems also seem much more feasible. An explosion of information exists in virtually every facet of daily life. Microchips and consumer electronics have brought us new intelligence. This intelligence, or ability to process large amounts of information for the benefit of individuals, has the potential for great benefit. As yet, road transportation and transit remain relatively unpenetrated by the information revolution that has altered many other aspects of work and leisure. Thus, a new transportation information infrastructure has the potential to dramatically increase the efficiency with which transportation resources are spent by individuals and society.

RESEARCH NEEDS

Research is needed to evaluate options for serving existing travel patterns, controlling demand, improving system performance, and restructuring the transportation network to better meet demand. A list of research needs is presented that relates to the material presented in this paper. This list represents one of several assigned points of departure for the more complete research agenda resulting from the conference.

The list of research needs begins with the premise that demand is not fixed. Transportation capacity is not being increased to accommodate some imagined fixed travel demand, as was the philosophy of the 1950s "Red Book" (7). Considerable progress has been made in recognizing and being able to predict how travel varies with its many long- and short-run determinants. The emphasis of the research needed now is on coordinating land use and transportation and understanding the total social costs at which various transportation options "produce" travel. It is necessary to know and plan for the many other factors besides transportation that affect land development. Better knowledge of the total social costs of travel will enable more informed investment decisions in transportation options and more equitable assessment of the costs of transportation improvements.

This list of research needs is therefore broken down into two parts:

1. Research about demand (Figure 1) and
2. Research quantifying the total social costs of travel (Figure 2).

Research About Demand

Research needs about demand relating to the paradigm in Figure 1 include the following questions:

- How do individuals react to information and travel conditions (costs) in their decisions to consume land and travel?
- How are resources and travel conditions likely to change in the future in terms of how these affect individual behavior?
- How are the population of individuals and their needs likely to change in the future?

Examples of more specific related research topics include the following questions:

- Do the new technologies in the list of options in Figure 3 affect demand in inherently different ways from currently available modes and technologies?
- How much of the recent increase in the percent of our incomes devoted to housing (from 20 percent to 40 percent in the past 40 years) has resulted from increases in interest rates, property taxes, utilities, and so forth, and how much is a real increase in price for the same or a higher-quality house?
- How have recent increases in urban traffic congestion affected the value of privately owned real estate?

- How does constraining parking availability (or other transportation services) below market demands affect the marketability of new urban development projects?
- Will improved information about travel choices cause travel to increase or decrease?
- What transportation options (including subsidies) can both improve travel conditions and reduce travel?
- What are possible strategies for internalizing certain social costs of travel that can be implemented in a politically fair and acceptable manner?
- How closely will "socially efficient" land use and travel distributions resemble those in today's cities?
- How closely will they if "socially efficient" is limited to the costs associated with travel (Figure 2)?

Research Quantifying Total Social Costs of Travel

Research needs relating to the private and social costs of travel (Figure 2) include the following questions:

- What are the components of the social costs of travel that are related to congestion?
- Are there major social costs of travel that are inversely related to congestion (e.g., the costs of socially inefficient land use distributions)?
- What are the values of the components of social costs of travel for different levels of travel and congestion?
- How do the social costs of travel vary with different strategies for internalizing them in decisions to consume land and travel?

Examples of more specific related research topics include

- Quantification of the private and social cost curves in Figure 2 for automobile congestion costs only (travel time and delay) for specific cities and travel corridors;
- Quantification of the relationship between automobile congestion and such externalities as air pollution, traffic accidents, noise pollution, and energy consumption;
- Determination of the relationship between automobile congestion and land value in U.S. cities;
- Determination, under current conditions of travel behavior and internalized travel costs, of the reductions in the total social costs of travel from increases in the capacity of conventional modes;

• Determination of whether any of the new technology options in Figure 3 promise significantly greater benefits from equivalent investments than increases in the capacity of currently available modes;

• Determination of what the incidence is of reductions in the social costs of travel from alternative investments and what the resulting implications are for more equitable assessments of the costs of infrastructure improvements;

• Determination of how much of the recent increases in congestion and the related social costs of travel in U.S. cities is caused by increased population density and how much is caused by increased trip lengths for certain segments of the population (e.g., lower-income families seeking cheaper housing on the periphery of metropolitan areas);

• What the benefits are from requiring that only those transportation investments be made whose costs are less than the benefits they provide from reducing the total social costs of travel; and

• Determination of possible loss of long-run benefits from travel if road pricing were used to internalize the social costs of travel.

REFERENCES

1. D. Brand. Theory and Method in Land Use and Travel Forecasting. In *Transportation Research Record 422*, TRB, National Research Council, Washington, D.C., pp. 10–20.
2. COMSIS Corporation. *Summary of Travel Trends, 1983–84 Nationwide Personal Transportation Study.* U.S. Department of Transportation, November 1985.
3. F. E. Jarema, S. Liss, and D. R. McElhaney. 1990 Nationwide Personal Transportation Study (NPTS): Current Status and Preliminary Results. Presented at 70th Annual Meeting of the Transportation Research Board, Washington, D.C., 1991.
4. E. B. Fisk. U.S. Says Most of Growth in 80's Was in Major Metropolitan Areas. *The New York Times,* February 21, 1991, p. A18.
5. C. Gibson. Respondents' Comments. In *Special Report 220: A Look Ahead: Year 2020.* TRB, National Research Council, Washington, D.C., 1988.
6. J. R. Stowers. Organizing and Funding Transportation for 2020, In *Special Report 220: A Look Ahead: Year 2020.* TRB, National Research Council, Washington, D.C., 1988.
7. *Road User Benefit Analyses for Highway Improvements.* AASHTO, Washington, D.C., 1960, 152 pp.

Site Design and Its Relation to Urban Form

MICHAEL V. DYETT
Blayney Dyett Greenberg, San Francisco, California

From the site planning and design perspective, the challenge is to heighten awareness of how different transportation solutions can be incorporated into physical plans for new residential, commercial, and industrial development. Local streets also need to be planned to be more than just automobile oriented. Provision for pedestrians, bus routes, and, where appropriate, rail transit needs to be made early in the planning process. This will require rethinking traditional subdivision design and layout of nonresidential areas.

BASIC UNDERSTANDING AND RELATIONSHIPS

City planners have gained a basic understanding about location decisions and urban form that comes from Alonso's *Location and Land Use* (*1*) and the theories of Hoyt (*2*), Hoover (*3*), Ricardo (*4*), and others. However, this body of theoretical work says little about how actual site design and layout and the interface between the private realm and the public realm can influence travel decisions beyond the obvious. If it is easy to find the place, park, and get around, then the business or retail center is likely to be patronized. People want convenience, not congestion. From a residential perspective, people seek neighborhoods that are within commuting distance of their work places and also offer convenient access to shopping, recreational opportunities, and local schools.

Academic research using census data, origin-destination surveys, and similar empirical data has yielded useful information about travel behavior that has helped practitioners construct travel demand

and mode-choice models, but these models provide few insights into how to configure land use at the neighborhood and community scale, both in developing urban areas and in older urban areas where intensification and "recycling" is occurring, in order to reduce automobile dependence and thus overall vehicle miles of travel.

Many professional city planners believe that more study of trip data is needed to understand the potential to eliminate or shorten trips of each type. Ease of transfers between modes of travel also is important, and more practical guidance is needed to show how to fit park-and-ride facilities, paratransit, bicycles, and buses into project designs. Two good models are the 1989 *Guide to Land Use and Public Transportation,* published by the U.S. Department of Transportation (5) and *Designing Urban Corridors,* a 1989 publication of the American Planning Association (6); however, more work needs to be done to demonstrate that such integration not only can be effective but also can be accomplished in a cost-effective fashion.

Architects and site planners follow rules for physical layout of new development that are established in zoning and subdivision ordinances. Traditional standards govern the location of a house or office building on a lot; they rarely require physical planners to think about relationships to transit or pedestrian linkages beyond the project itself. Similarly, signage often is done last, and the functional and directional relationships within a project and between a project and adjacent development are not always worked out (e.g., walks to lunch spots, walks to transit, outdoor eating areas).

Urban planners do not know a lot about how to make mixed use work at less than the "mega-scale"—to strike the right balance in urban and suburban areas, particularly where neighborhoods and commercial districts are recycling, and to encourage sharing amenities between commercial and residential areas.

Both urban planners and transportation planners need to work within the framework of the built environment and identify different solutions for different types of urban and suburban areas. One example of a relatively successful program is in San Diego, California, where the Office of the City Architect, working with the Engineering and Development Department and the Metropolitan Transit Board, has initiated specific guidelines for transportation demand management (TDM) in the central business district, suburban employment centers, and transit-oriented corridors (7). The principal characteristics sought for each of these areas are illustrated in Figure 1. To complement this effort, citywide street design standards also have been established, including requirements for

- Sidewalks on both sides of all streets;
- Driveway limits (number and width);
- Sidewalks buffered from traffic;
- Pedestrian-oriented lighting;
- Minimal use of cul-de-sacs;
- Preference for loop roads, alleys, and cross streets; and
- Bicycle facilities, where appropriate.

Work being done currently shows specific options for site design, parking, transportation facilities and services, and support services that should be considered for typical projects (see Figure 2). These

Central Business District

- Highest FARs; very-high residential density
- Mixed-use
- Pedestrian-oriented buildings
- Underground or enclosed parking
- Parking maximums

Suburban Employment Centers

- High FARs; high residential density
- Mixed use
- On-site support services
- Pedestrian-oriented site plans
- Parking underground, or to rear or side
- Parking to vary according to transit proximity
- Parking maximums

Transit-Oriented Corridors

- Moderate-high intensity use
- Pedestrian-oriented development
- Parking management required

FIGURE 1 San Diego: land guidance for TDM program (7).

	Regional	Community	Neighborhood	Mixed/Residential	Large Offices	Small Offices	Business Park	Industry
Site Design								
Pedestrian Orientation	●	●	●	●	●	●	●	●
Transit Access	●	●		●	●		●	●
Carpool/Vanpool Waiting Area	●				●		●	●
Parking								
Carpool/Vanpool Parking	●				●		●	●
Paid Parking	●				●		●	●
Limited Access to Parking	●				●		●	●
Shared Parking	●			●	●			
Transportation Facilities								
Bus Shelter	●	●		●	●		●	●
Transit/HOV Facilities	●				●		●	
Bike Racks/Lockers	●	●	●	●	●	●	●	●
Bike Lanes/Paths	●				●		●	
Electric/Alternative Fuel	●				●		●	
Transportation Services								
Information: Kiosk or Counter	●	●		●	●		●	
Information: Bulletin Board			●			●		●
Support Services								
Childcare	●						●	
Teleconferencing Facilities					●		●	●
Shower/Locker Facilities	●				●		●	●
Other Commercial Services	●	●		●	●		●	●
Size (in 000s sq. ft.)	1,000	200	25	200	500	25	1,000	200

FIGURE 2 San Diego: developer options for typical projects (7).

requirements are being fleshed out in more detail, for possible incorporation into the city's zoning ordinance.

In northern California, Sacramento County has taken the concept of integrating transportation and land use planning a step further by defining a specific type of transit-oriented development (TOD) as part of a growth strategy required by the newly adopted General Plan (8). The objective of the TOD program is to concentrate moderate and high-density housing in mixed-use clusters centered around regional transit station stops. Neighborhood TODs may be as small as 40 acres, whereas urban TODs could be as large as 160 acres (Figure 3). The county anticipates that TODs would be developed in infill locations as well as in new urban growth areas.

To promote transit access, local streets are to be designed to converge on transit stops and core commercial areas; there should be minimal need for cul-de-sacs, and multiple and parallel routes would serve automobiles, bicycles, and pedestrians (Figure 4). An arterial

Size: 40 - 160 Acres
Maximum Distance from Transit: 2000 Ft.

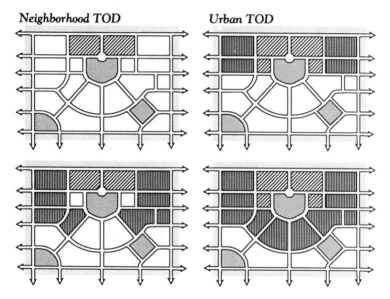

Percent of Site Area

Use	Neighborhood TOD	Urban TOD
Public	10% minimum	10% minimum
Core*	10-15%	10-30%
Housing	40-80%	20-60%
Office	0-40%	20-60%

* Minimum retail space: 10,000 sq. ft.

FIGURE 3 Sacramento County transit-oriented development (TOD) *(8)*.

Preferred

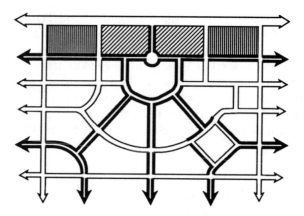

Interconnected streets converging to transit stop and
core commercial. Minimal need for cul-de-sacs.

Prohibited

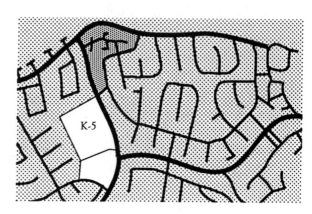

FIGURE 4 Sacramento County transit-oriented development street patterns (8).

street should not be the sole route between neighborhoods, as is
typically the case in traditional subdivisions.

To reduce automobile use for most shopping trips, it may be pro-
ductive to encourage construction of more, smaller shopping centers
instead of fewer, larger centers, which is the current trend. If such
centers are well served by transit or located near park-and-ride facilities, the chance of success may be higher than if they are only served
by highways and arterials. California cities such as Davis and Oceanside

have set limits on the size of neighborhood and community-oriented commercial centers to encourage this type of development pattern.

Last, urban planners and site designers could be well rewarded with a better understanding of the importance of project identity for neighborhood cohesion and spatial orientation, that is, what organizing elements at the project scale can help reinforce larger elements of urban form and support a balanced transportation system. Current practice is to focus solely on the developers' market and immediate land use relationships, with less attention given to regional access and ease of transit service. The TOD program in Sacramento County and San Diego's Developer Handbook (7) are intended to spur awareness of these linkages.

METHODOLOGY

To help in plan-making, urban planners need better guidance (rules of thumb) to make decisions on land use mix and minimum density versus intensity that will support different types of transit use. This information also will prove useful in project review by providing a clearer frame of reference for developers and their architects about what constitutes acceptable, transit-oriented developments.

With the growing importance of traffic congestion as a community issue, urban planners need more information about the strengths and weaknesses of level-of-service (LOS) standards as a growth management tool and criterion for project review. Although LOS can establish specific measures against which to judge a project's impact on road operations and measure effectiveness, these standards often are mandated without regard to whether they can be attained; they are unable to control demand or, in many cases, capacity; finally, they do not permit trade-offs that accept congestion at some locations. This is important because congestion is "needed" in order to increase use of alternative modes. In the San Francisco Bay Area, alternative approaches to using LOS standards for regional routes have been devised as part of Contra Costa County's growth management and transportation improvement program (9). These may prove to be useful guides for other jurisdictions seeking flexibility in fitting transportation solutions to land use patterns.

To improve administration of transit-oriented development policies, planners need more practical guidance on how to structure surveys of specific types of projects to gauge parking demand, correlate

TDM measures and parking use, and ensure effective monitoring of conditions of project approval. Such programs also are required to ensure compliance with environmental laws calling for mitigation monitoring and reporting following certification of environmental documents such as an environmental impact review or an environmental impact statement.

Finally, information on effective ways to provide for collective use of parking facilities and also encourage transit use also would help. Here, the methodological issue can help address a policy question— whether local incentives or regulations can bring park-and-ride opportunities into underused commercial centers, both to increase transit ridership and to help local merchants. Normally, zoning ordinances do not allow a parking standard, the number of spaces required per 1,000 square feet of commercial space, to be reduced because transit service is available or to recognize joint use of parking areas for commuter parking as well as shopping.

POLICY AND INSTITUTIONS

Local decision-makers can learn from more detailed guidance on site planning, parking management, and project design and its relation to circulation systems and transit. Case studies and comparative surveys could show the merit of parking maximums as well as parking minimums in zoning ordinances. Such information also would help local officials determine whether, as a matter of local development policy, there should be a "lid" on downtown parking or parking around transit nodes in order to encourage transit use. In Portland, Oregon, for example, the number of parking spaces has been limited for more than a decade. By contrast, parking limits for commercial development around stations on San Francisco's Bay Area Rapid Transit (BART) system have rarely been set. In fact, commuter parking spillover has prompted complaints for more local parking.

As a general rule, it may make sense to encourage urban planners and traffic engineers to make streets narrower in newly developing neighborhoods. They also should ensure that in shopping centers and business parks internal roads can accommodate a 40-ft bus. If such standards are not imposed, then efforts to encourage transit service in suburban employment centers will be less successful, because convenient door-to-door service cannot be provided.

Narrower streets slow traffic, make walking more pleasant, and improve the scale of residential, commercial, and industrial areas.

These objectives are clearly being sought in the San Diego and Sacramento County programs.

To emphasize a pedestrian scale, not just in pockets but throughout the community, urban planners should require sidewalks in all new subdivisions and in commercial and industrial development. A corollary should be no more "gated communities." To further create a streetscape for walking, zoning ordinances should require that parking in neighborhood commercial areas be placed in back of buildings. Making buildings address the street improves the appearance of cities and encourages walking.

Finally, local planners and officials need more information about new types of transit-oriented zoning and development regulations, including incentives or bonuses to improve the quality of higher-density housing and office complexes near transit nodes to make them desirable. It is not sufficient to provide just a certain amount of housing near jobs; it also is necessary to provide the right kind and mix. This issue was central to the debate at this conference over appropriate land use in the business park corridor adjacent to John Wayne Airport (*10*).

RESEARCH NEEDS

To guide preparation of a research agenda for FHWA, the following questions are suggested as promising avenues of inquiry:

- What are appropriate site development standards to address pedestrian, bicycle, and transit availability?
- How effective are density "floors" that set a minimum land use intensity and parking "lids" in encouraging transit use?
- How should commercial and industrial parking requirements vary based on transit availability?
- What are the minimum requirements for support services and eating and drinking establishments at major employment centers to affect work-based vehicle trips?
- What street design standards encourage pedestrian use and bicycling?
- How should conflicts between the goals of reducing peak-hour congestion and improving air quality be reconciled?

Air quality-related transportation measures are intended to reduce vehicle trips, whereas congestion-reduction measures focus on increasing capacity or spreading trips throughout the day, or both. Either one of these approaches could have the unintended effect of a net increase in vehicle trips. Specific guidance is needed for site planning and project review, so priorities and trade-offs are understood. This is particularly important for local officials and for developers who are attempting to reconcile competing considerations in an uncertain economic environment.

REFERENCES

1. W. Alonso. *Location and Land Use: Toward a General Theory of Land Rent.* Harvard University Press, Cambridge, 1964.
2. H. Hoyt. *The Structure and Growth of Residential Neighborhoods in American Cities.* Government Printing Office, Washington, D.C., 1939.
3. E. M. Hoover. *The Location of Economic Activity.* McGraw-Hill, New York, N.Y., 1948.
4. D. Ricardo. *On the Principles of Political Economy and Taxation.* London, 1817.
5. Snohomish County Transportation Authority. *A Guide to Land Use and Public Transportation.* Report DOT-T-90-13. U. S. Department of Transportation, December 1989.
6. K. R. Bishop. *Designing Urban Corridors.* Planning Advisory Service Report 418. American Planning Association, Chicago, Ill., 1989.
7. *Transportation Demand Management Developer Handbook.* Office of the City Architect, City of San Diego, September 1990.
8. Calthorpe and Associates. *Transit-Oriented Development Design Guidelines.* Final Review Draft, Sacramento County Planning and Community Development Department, September 1990.
9. *Growth Management Program Implementation Documents: LOS Guide, Model Growth Management Element, Guide to Local Planning and Growth Management.* Contra Costa Transportation Authority, Walnut Creek, California, August 1990; October 1990.
10. *Irvine Business Complex Urban Village Project.* Review Draft, City of Irvine Community Development Department, September 1989.

3
Workshop Reports

Workshop 1

CHAIR: Alan E. Pisarski
SECRETARY: Frederick W. Ducca
PARTICIPANTS: Trina T. Belanger, Daniel E. Benson, Michael V. Dyett, Donald Emerson, Deborah Gordon, Gary Hawthorn, Richard Horne, Charles Lave, Patrick McCue, Douglas R. Porter, James P. Reichert, Jerry Skillette, Richard Tustian

In Workshop 1, the research projects outlined in the following sections were raised.

UNDERSTANDING THE LAND USE–TRANSPORTATION DECISION PROCESS

There have been many changes during the past 20 years in demographics, including household size, composition, work force participation, and work force composition. These changes have influenced location decisions, but it is not known how or to what extent. The research project proposed would be an in-depth behavioral survey to determine how households currently make location decisions. Included in this survey would be the relative importance of transportation in the location decision compared with other factors, such as schools and neighborhood type. In addition to location decisions, the survey would cover how transportation decisions such as type of mode, time of day, and destination are made. A by-product of this project would be data to support a combined location and mode-choice modeling process.

EFFECTIVENESS OF PLANNING INSTITUTIONS

The quality of planning and the ability to implement plans depend on the organizational and institutional environment in which plans are

129

made. For example, areas with geographically large jurisdictions may find it easier to implement plans than do areas that have many fragmented jurisdictions. Different types of metropolitan planning organizations (MPOs) and staffing may result in different types of planning. The institutions should be cross-classified by area type, degree of control, organizational structure, and state of the regional economy. Also included should be institutional relationships between different levels of government. Overall, the research would address what types of organizational and institutional arrangements produce the best planning results.

EFFECTIVENESS OF GROWTH MANAGEMENT

Many options are available for growth management, including restrictive zoning, taxes, and impact fees. The proposed research project would identify the various options for growth management and evaluate their probable effectiveness. It would also identify side effects of the various options. Options would be described in terms of the type of environment in which they were applied, such as regionwide or subarea, and the type of region, such as growing or declining. The economic, social, and political costs of each option would be described. The project would be useful to local and state governments considering growth management efforts.

TRIP MAKING AND LAND USE TYPE

How do different types of land use affect trip-making behavior? For example, do higher-density centers promote transit, pedestrian, and carpool trips? If so, to what extent? This question needs to be answered for different categories of land use, such as residential, commercial, and retail.

PREFERRED TYPES OF HOUSING AND LAND USE

It has been said that everyone wants a detached house in the suburbs on a quarter acre of land. Is this the most desirable pattern, or is this pattern chosen because of other amenities that go along with it, such as a good school system? The proposed project would attempt to identify preferred types of housing by type of locator. Locator categories would include age, phase in the life-cycle, marital status, and so forth. The results would be useful to zoning boards making decisions on the type of land use allowed in their communities.

COST OF SPRAWL

What is the true cost of our current land use patterns, including social, environmental, and political costs? Costs would be estimated for different types of land uses, from dense central business district to suburban sprawl.

NEW DESIGNS, OLDER CITIES

One of the issues in urban development will be retrofitting existing centers with new designs that are more transportation friendly. How can these new designs be made to work when fit on top of existing infrastructure?

JOBS-HOUSING BALANCE

Much has been said about the problem of the jobs-housing balance. What is the transportation benefit of redressing an imbalance between jobs and housing? If everyone were moved to locations as close as possible to their jobs, how would transportation improve? Also, useful measures of the jobs-housing balance need to be developed. Jobs and housing may be in perfect balance, but people who live in an area may not be the same people who work there. Measures of the jobs-housing balance need to be disaggregated by income group and perhaps other factors. What would be appropriate measures for the jobs-housing balance?

IMPEDIMENTS TO LOCATION SHIFT

There are many impediments, both to the individual and the firm, to shifting location. Among these are real estate transfer taxes, costs of selling a home, and low interest rates associated with homes owned for a period of time. Similarly, factors such as pension benefits and job security may prevent individuals from shifting jobs. This research would identify these impediments and establish the relative influence of each.

WORK SITE LOCATIONAL PREFERENCES

What are the locational preferences of workers and corporations? In addition to the trip to work, many other purposes may be satisfied by the commute, such as convenience shopping, banking, and daycare. What amenities do employees want at the work site? Do employees prefer low-density centers or high-density centers, urban or suburban locations? Different sizes and types of firms have varying location preferences. Some may be more sensitive to the cost of land, whereas others may want good transportation access for workers. How do these preferences vary by size of firm, type of firm, type of worker, and life-cycle of the firm?

AIR QUALITY AND CONGESTION

What are the true long-term and short-term air quality effects of congestion reduction measures? Relieving congestion may improve air quality by decreasing the amount of time the engine is in operation and allowing traffic to operate at a higher speed. Simultaneously, reduced congestion may induce additional trips or allow for longer trips in the same amount of time. In the very long run, improving travel time may promote new development. It is important to understand all of these interactive effects on air quality.

CONFLICT RESOLUTION AND MEDIATION

In many areas there is conflict among local governments or between local and state governments concerning the planning and decision making process. What can conflict resolution techniques and mediation techniques do to help moderate this conflict? Along with this, are there alternative models of government or cooperative arrangements that can streamline the decision making process or implementation of plans?

FINANCE

Several different finance research questions emerged.

New Transportation Roles

With the slowdown in development and downturn in the economy, revenue from nontraditional sources such as impact fees and special assessment districts may be declining. What new demands for transportation will be placed on traditional financing sources? Further, with money scarcer, revenue sources such as impact fees will come under closer scrutiny by both the public and private sectors. What will be the effect of this?

Aggregation of Sources

Impact fees and special assessment districts require that funds be spent either for specific improvements or improvements in a specific area. This often results in many small accounts that cannot be spent fully. What are alternative funding or legal mechanisms to allow aggregation of these funds?

Alternative Financing Contribution

Impact fees, special assessment districts, toll roads, and other innovative financing mechanisms have often been seen as a substitute for more traditional financing measures. What is the overall contribution of alternative financing to infrastructure needs? How does the amount of funding available through alternative financing compare with total fiscal requirements? What portion of needs must be met by traditional revenue sources?

Effect of Revenue Measures on Transportation

Some revenue-raising measures may have negative effects on transportation. Real estate transfer taxes may keep workers from relocating close to the work site, and revenue raised from property taxes encourages development patterns that may not be well served by transportation. At the same time, gasoline taxes can promote more fuel-efficient cars and less driving. The proposed project would look at various mechanisms for raising revenue and analyze their effects on transportation.

DATA NEEDS

There was general agreement that more data are needed and more empirical studies need to be done. The following are the recommended projects.

Private Sector Data

The adequacy of private sector data sources needs to be assessed. This includes employment data, such as Dun & Bradstreet and Polk's. Other private sector data sources should be identified and their utility for transportation planning identified.

Empirical Studies

Empirical studies are needed on density patterns in the United States. At what levels of density are people living? Empirical research is also needed on the relationship of land use and transportation. To what extent do improvements in transportation draw development? What is the time frame for land use to respond to transportation changes?

Better Data Bases

Current home interview data bases in most areas are 20 to 25 years old. These need to be updated. Further, it is not known how location decisions currently are being made. More data need to be collected to determine this.

Longitudinal Studies

Longitudinal data are also needed. Empirical studies, over time, of how improvements in transportation infrastructure affect land use need to be done. An example would be tracking development patterns after a highway has been built. One of the questions to be answered would be how long it takes for land use to respond to transportation improvements.

Downtown Growth

Empirical data on growth in the downtown areas need to be collected. Along with this, methods need to be developed to project this growth.

HOUSING SUBSIDIES

Housing subsidies occur at many different income levels. They occur through the public sector at lower income levels. At higher income levels they may also occur through the private sector (e.g., subsidies involved with employer relocation). The deductibility of interest paid on mortgages may also act as a housing subsidy. The proposed project would examine housing subsidies and identify the effect they have on housing location.

INCOME AND HOUSING PRICE

What is the relationship of income, housing price, and housing location? The proposed project would identify the trade-offs made between type of neighborhood, type of housing, travel time, and income.

AIR QUALITY MODELING

What are the full economic, social, and environmental costs associated with maintaining various levels of air quality? What are the costs of not maintaining air quality?

AIR QUALITY MONITORING

An assessment of the adequacy of current methods of monitoring air quality needs to be done, including data sets to support the monitoring.

PUBLIC POLICY AND PRIVATE DECISIONS

In many areas public policy may be in conflict with private desires. For example, zoning regulations may encourage low density, single-family housing, but not all may want it. Public policy may also be in conflict with itself; there may be a public policy to encourage ridesharing and at the same time public policy to require large amounts of parking at development sites. The proposed project would identify public policies affecting transportation, individual desires, and areas in which these are in conflict.

Workshop 2

CHAIR: George V. Wickstrom
SECRETARY: Christopher Fleet
PARTICIPANTS: Elizabeth A. Deakin, Hugh Fitzpatrick, Richard
S. Glaze, John R. Hamburg, Lynne B. Judd, Barna Juhasz,
Veronica Kuhn, Eugene J. Lessieu, Ken Ogden

Workshop 2 had two main phases:

1. General discussion and sharing of ideas based on individual
members' backgrounds and professional roles as well as on the six
resource papers and
2. The development of more specific research needs statements.

INITIAL DISCUSSION AND SHARING OF IDEAS

The initial discussion was generally free form in that members were
encouraged to offer a wide range of ideas, needs, and current problems. Because a wide range of professional backgrounds was repre-
sented, there was an equally wide range of ideas on research needs.
The following is a list, by member, of most of the topics presented
and discussed by the group:

Veronica Kuhn of the Natural Resources Defense Council focused on

- Analysis of the energy impacts of congestion.
- Analysis of the relationship between congestion and air quality, including the benefits of vehicle miles traveled (VMT) and
peak-period congestion reduction.
- Determination of possible air pollution reduction resulting from
a transportation demand management (TDM) strategy and the
overcoming of problems associated with the acceptance by the state

136

department of transportation of a transportation strategy developed by the air quality district.

- A study of automobile use and ownership versus land use density (the Natural Resources Defense Council conducted a study that showed a one-third reduction in VMT from a doubling of land use density) plus a determination of what the benefits are of achieving a shorter trip versus dropping a trip.

Richard Glaze of Harland Bartholomew & Associates focused on

- Determination of whether transit-friendly design reduces automobile trip making.
- Examination of site design concepts to determine why sites are designed as they are.
- Determination of the reasonable effect on travel demand of a site designed for pedestrian use.

Gene Lessieu of the Port Authority of New York & New Jersey focused on

- Examination of the concept of capacity.
- Definition of congestion.

John Hamburg of Barton Aschman Associates focused on

- Current knowledge about how transportation works and measurement of transportation and land use.
- Determination of the future settlement patterns.
- Determination of the role of transportation planners and how effective they can be. Communities are "pushed" into settlement patterns by economic forces (i.e., driven by greed). The result is that transportation impacts are not what is expected. Transportation cannot influence land use if the real development forces are not understood.
- Analysis of land use and transportation by corridors. As technology changes over time, the latest technology can be introduced in the corridor being analyzed for alternative transportation modes.

Ken Ogden of the University of California, Irvine, focused on

- The failure of pricing, which leads to congestion.
- Goods movement, which is 50 percent of the cost of urban transportation.

- Determination of whether telecommunications is a substitute or a stimulus for travel and what the individual vehicle of the future will look like.
- Determination of what groups of people are affected by mobility constraints or the quality of travel.
- Formulation of a time frame for research that determines what can be done now and what can be done later.

Hugh Fitzpatrick of The Irvine Company focused on

- Determination of the region-specific information needs (with emphasis on local information systems).
- Determination of the constraints (air quality, water, labor, etc.) and the "pressure points," including analysis of where it matters.

Lynne Judd of the Wisconsin Department of Transportation focused on

- Analysis of what people want in housing, including what is important and what their relation to density is.
- Acquisition of methods of evaluation, including how to measure nonuser benefits, effects, and factors and how to get these factors into the planning process.
- Determination of regional data needs (with the credibility of local data being called into question, longitudinal analysis of travel behavior is needed).

Elizabeth Deakin of the University of California, Berkeley, focused on

- Determination of how to remove the institutional barriers affecting pricing, analysis of problems affecting the feasibility of implementation, and determination of the implications of pricing for environmental concerns.
- Determination of the land use/environmental effects of increased capacity resulting from intelligent vehicle/ highway systems (IVHS).
- Acquisition of data to conduct research.
- Determination of data collection methodology for transportation studies.
- Determination of how to eliminate the gap that exists between research and practice.
- Analysis of institutional structure and change, including how to conduct research on institutions (e.g., improved coordination, commun-

ications) and how to manage work within and among various organizations involved in the urban planning process (i.e., what has worked and what has not).

ADDITIONAL DISCUSSION ITEMS

Additional discussion items included the following:

- The effect of federal financing policies (e.g., federal matching ratios) on urban transportation and form.
- The measurement and evaluation of the quality of system and travel.
- Determination of the role of the transportation planner, including how much planners can be expected to do; how to keep up with changing technical procedures; and the education needs of planning staffs.
- Analysis of the scale of planning, focusing on what percent of VMT is affected.

DEVELOPMENT OF RESEARCH STATEMENTS

Out of the roundtable discussion in the workshop, members identified and picked subject areas for which they would draft project problem statements and research objectives. The assignments were as follows:

- Veronica Kuhn was assigned the impacts of congestion relief on air quality, the effect of TDM measures, and the impact on air quality of trip length versus the number of trips.
- Richard Glaze was assigned right-of-way protection and access management.
- Gene Lessieu was assigned measurement of the impact of congestion on urban form.
- John Hamburg was assigned management and coordination of scale and data in land use and transportation planning.
- Ken Ogden was assigned goods movement.
- Hugh Fitzpatrick was assigned institutional issues associated with implementation of regional transportation and land use plans.
- Lynne Judd was assigned evaluation and measurement of nonuser benefits.

- Elizabeth Deakin was assigned implication of pricing and technology on location and urban structure.
- George Wickstrom was assigned effectiveness and limitations of metropolitan planning organizations (MPOs).

RESEARCH NEEDS

Fourteen research proposals were developed in this workshop group. They covered 12 main topics and were grouped into the following six research areas.

Governance and Institutional Considerations

Governance

Problem

Governance (the assignment of responsibilities for land use, transportation, and air quality planning and programming to specific agencies) has significant but poorly understood effects on the ability of a region to achieve its most important environmental and social goals. For example, responsibility for land use densities and parking typically is given to local governments. Responsibility for developing and implementing transportation plans and programs usually rests with MPOs and the state. The level of mobile source emissions is the responsibility of air quality districts, the state, and the U.S. Environmental Protection Agency.

These agencies have different areas of jurisdiction, different mandates and priorities, and overlapping or contradictory authority. The manner in which decision making occurs within these agencies and their relationships among each other will significantly affect a region's ability to meet goals such as assuring the provision of an adequate transportation system; meeting state and national ambient air quality standards; providing an adequate supply of housing, schools, and recreational facilities; and sustaining the regional economy.

Need

There is an urgent need to examine alternative modes of governance that permit regions to harmonize and optimize competing social and environmental goals. In particular, identification of the assignment of technical responsibilities that have a significant impact on policy decisions is urgently needed. "Models" need to be provided for methods of dealing with governance issues in very large, large, medium, and small urban areas.

Research

Case studies need to be developed on how specific metropolitan areas assign authority for land use, transportation, and air quality. Theoretical models of governance need to be developed that address issues such as what constitutes a manageable unit of government, conflict resolution, efficiency in planning and decision making, social equity, and legitimacy.

Effectiveness and Limitations of Metropolitan Planning Organizations

Problem

Over the past two decades the ability of MPOs to respond to key urban issues has been affected both by reductions in the funding available and the introduction of a variety of new issues requiring attention. Only the largest metropolitan regions have been able to maintain a basic capability to collect and analyze data and prepare sound forecasts and analyses.

Need

There is a need to review the effectiveness and limitations of MPOs with regard to providing data, methodology, forecasts, analysis, and support to decision makers and citizens in urbanized areas. Options available to MPOs to address the issues of land use form and density, transportation facilities and services, and the environmental implications of proposed actions need to be identified and understood.

Research is needed to evaluate the current limitations of MPOs and identify areas in which improvement in organization, approach, and focus can permit an expanded capability to deal at acceptable cost with emerging planning issues in land use, transportation, and the environment.

Research

A national sample of MPOS, both large and small, should be selected and past work programs, budgets, and staff skills obtained and presented. End products would be categorized over time and the levels of effort needed would be quantified. In addition, a brief description of the functions, data, and techniques used would be given. Interviews would be conducted either by mail or in person with the MPO director and staff. Data processing and computing capacity and the use of consultant or state and local support would also be reviewed.

A comparative analysis should be conducted of the degree to which MPOs are addressing current and emerging issues; the level and nature of funding; and the relative nature, scale, and currency of the data base, along with an analysis of forecasting and analytical ability and staff skills and experience.

The result of this research would not be specific recommendations to individual MPOs but an overall statement of the state of the practice that would be related to the scale and nature of the problems identified by the MPO directors. A report would be prepared assessing priority needs along with opportunities for improvements.

Congestion Management, Pricing, and Nonuser Benefits

Effects of Congestion Management on Air Quality

Problem

In nonattainment areas air pollution control plans require reductions in automobile emissions. Congestion management is often proposed as a means to achieve this, but the potential effectiveness of such measures is not fully known.

Need

There is a need to assess the potential effectiveness of congestion management actions in order to choose between transportation options and to predict the effectiveness of air pollution control plans.

Research

This research would quantify the effects of congestion management on automobile emissions and energy use, especially as they relate to land use issues.

Impacts of Highway Pricing on Urban Form

Problem

Advances in electronics and computers have made automated road pricing a technologically feasible option. However, proposals for widespread institution of tolls face considerable challenges. Concerns include the potential for adverse traffic and other impacts on alternative, untolled routes, worries about loss of privacy if pricing becomes ubiquitous and billings are based on roadside monitoring of trips, and, in particular, objections to the disparity of impact as a function of income (the heavy burden falling on low and moderate income highway users).

A longer-term issue is how road pricing might affect urban form. Possible responses to road pricing would be to shift the time of travel to less congested periods; share a ride in order to share costs; shift to another, less expensive route; shift to an unaffected mode; reduce trip frequency; shift to destinations with lower access costs; or relocate to avoid high travel costs altogether. The last two possibilities, in particular, could have significant implications for urban form. However, the likelihood that such effects actually would occur, their timing, and their magnitude would depend on relative prices within the region, the availability and quality of travel alternatives, and the treatment of equity issues, as well as on other factors, including the nature of the urban economy and housing.

Need

Comprehensive research is needed to explore fully the issues related to highway pricing. These include the "spillover" problem when traffic is diverted to untolled facilities, privacy issues related to the monitoring and collecting of billing data, and the equity issue of who is affected by the pricing strategies. The impact of pricing on urban form must also be analyzed and quantified.

Research

The following areas would be included in this research:

- Estimation of prices needed to fulfill intended objectives (efficient operation, capturing of emissions costs, etc.);

- Exploration of equity consequences (by income, race, sex) of various pricing strategies;
- Exploration of alternative ways to use revenue (e.g., efficient levels of road building; alternative modes; payments for programs focusing on air pollution, safety. etc.; redistributive strategies to offset income-based impacts of prices);
- Examination of institutional issues associated with pricing or not pricing different functional classes of urban highways; and
- Consolidation of the above into a set of plausible scenarios and analysis of the impact on trip generation, mode choice, trip distribution, location choice, and environmental quality.

Evaluation of Nonuser Benefits and Disbenefits

Problem

Nonuser benefits and disbenefits are valued by society and are receiving increased attention and being accorded increased importance in debates about transportation investments. Consideration of these factors has not been institutionalized or has not been institutionalized in a consistent manner by transportation agencies. Valid measures of these impacts need to be developed and methods for their consideration need to be agreed on by agencies with a stake in decisions. Foremost among these are air quality impacts because of federal regulations demanding their consideration, but water resources and questions about urban form and neighborhood integrity also merit attention.

Need

There is a need to develop valid measures of nonuser benefits and a basic understanding of relationships that reflect true value and can be used with measures of user benefits. There is also a need to integrate measures easily and effectively into project selection and prioritization processes used by all levels of government.

Research

Research elements include the following:

- Identification of major nonuser benefits;
- Determination of the status of knowledge about basic relationships;

- Identification and evaluation of measurement options (nominal, ordinal, interval; appropriate scale and units) in light of the status of knowledge (and uncertainty); and
- Development and evaluation of options for integrating measures into transportation decision processes (project, system, or program level). Issues include the nature of the process (formal, informal), timing (early, late), and incorporating measures in the process as part of alternative development or integrating when priority is determined, and so forth.

As part of this research, a survey of literature, assessment of current knowledge, and identification of remaining basic research needs should be conducted. Information about and a description of project decision processes should also be included.

Urban Design-Travel Interaction

Density Levels and Land Use Mix

Problem

Questions have been posed about whether congestion (or its impact in terms of travel delays, energy use, and air quality) varies significantly with different land use densities or patterns. But transportation consequences of various schemes for growth management and mixed-use zoning and design strategies are not well understood by land use and transportation planners, zoning officials, and community and regional planners.

Need

It is necessary to understand the effects of alternative land use patterns on at least three different aspects of transportation demand: total trip generation and VMT, length of trips, and mode choice. In addition, land use planners, zoning officials, and community leaders are not able to quantify and evaluate with ease the impacts of various mixes and densities of land use resulting from zoning and design strategies. Generalizations about the costs of congestion and resulting "waste" and air pollution problems need to be analyzed and quantified.

Research

This research should be designed to address the question of whether the impacts of congestion vary significantly with urban form and the effects of those patterns and mixes on travel demand. More specifically, it should determine whether, for example, it is more economically efficient to redesign the automobile (i.e., more energy efficient, less polluting) than to redesign the city, whether any or all forms of urban development meet individual and accumulated travel time budgets within a certain range of "acceptability," or whether major public transit projects are more or less "neutral" in their impact on either congestion or urban form.

As a part of this research, congestion and urban form would be correlated to determine the relationship and the magnitude of that relationship. The definition of "congestion" would be assessed in terms of such measures as overall system configuration, overall transportation system service, average travel time by trip purpose, change in average travel time caused by congestion, and causes of congestion (i.e., capacity, incidents, reconstruction). Urban form would be defined by such items as overall size of the region, corridors that are "average" or unique, residential and employment density, journey-to-work trip characteristics (e.g., average distance, speed, time, mode), and other travel demand characteristics.

This research would identify the magnitude of impact and the way in which land use decisions alter transportation demand in order to assess the air quality impacts of different urban forms. It would assess the effects of the proximity of different land use mixes on travel demand (e.g., how many trips are eliminated and how automobile ownership is affected).

Individual Choice

Problem

Objectives and goals for transportation and land use are often established according to planners' perceptions about predominant tastes and preferences of individuals. The impacts of individual choices and preferences of residence and location, access to housing, travel, recreation, and other amenities is not well understood, nor is it incorporated into the planning process.

Need

There is a need to assess the impacts and possibilities of using transportation as a "motive force" to create livable cities, rather than as a demand-derived service.

Research

This research should be oriented to maximize individual choice and create desirable environments within an urban configuration designed to minimize travel demand and environmental disruption. The research should explore what the features are of a concentrated, diverse, transit-intensive urban structure that create a desirable urban habitat.

Right-of-Way Protection and Access Management

Problem

The primary inadequacy of adopted transportation system plans in the past two decades has been the inability to construct the improvements identified in the plans. Generally, the land use and socioeconomic forecasts and the planned system configurations have been reasonable and consistent. However, major elements of the plans have not been constructed, primarily because of inadequate financial resources. An increasingly elongated planning and design process has also delayed projects when construction funds were available.

Development activity during the periods of delayed construction has often precluded the eventual construction of planned facilities. Right-of-way costs have become increasingly prohibitive when construction funds or location approval were eventually obtained, either substantially raising the cost of the improvement or causing the project to be canceled or scaled down.

Need

Because construction funds will probably always lag behind "needs," mechanisms must be developed to protect right-of-way for planned facilities and to manage the access to major facilities so that they will function as intended. Such mechanisms, if successfully employed, would minimize the share of transportation investment funds required for land acquisition.

Land regulation is a function of local governments. Most have sufficient land regulation authority to implement some form of successful right-of-way protection, provided that there is sufficient understanding of the need and that the political will to carry out such a program exists. In some jurisdictions, state enabling legislation may be required. Particularly in areas where right-of-way acquisition costs are approaching 50 percent of facility capital costs, such programs would have the result of stretching limited transportation resources across more projects. As a result, a larger share of the planned system would be built when needed and would function as intended.

Research

Right-of-way protection is achievable through a variety of means, including

- Reservation in local government land use plans, zoning instrument and decisions, and subdivision design and approval processes;
- Dedication of corridor rights-of-way as part of development approval processes;
- Temporary/permanent easements;
- Acquisition; and
- Access control.

Case studies of the benefits and costs of protecting rights-of-way through each type of mechanism in jurisdictions where they have been or are being used will provide data for comparison with results of case studies of areas where these mechanisms are not used. An analysis of the legal and process issues could clarify the applicability of techniques under current or modified federal and state laws. These issues include fundamental property rights, the potential for "prejudicing" ultimate location/design decisions, and maintenance responsibilities and costs before construction.

Access management issues to be addressed include the degradation of facility capacity from the provision of access permits not consistent with the intended function of the facility, the legal ramifications of providing system (instead of facility) access, and the overall maintenance of the functional integrity of constructed facilities.

Modeling and Data

New Directions in Urban Land Use and Transportation Modeling

Problem

Over the past two decades advances in computers, in data base management, and in graphical representation have reduced modeling time and cost requirements and have enabled more efficient and insightful use of information. Conceptual advances also have been made, resulting in stronger capabilities in modeling travel behavior and location choice. However, few practitioners have taken full advantage of these advances, and many urban areas continue to apply simplified models whose form and structure were developed 20 years ago or earlier.

Need

The utility and adequacy of available models increasingly are being questioned because of their inability to adequately address current land use and environmental policy issues for rail transit and for highway projects. The ability to model and analytically asses these issues is of particular importance in areas that have not yet attained the national ambient air quality standards and therefore will be required to demonstrate that their transportation plans and short-term programs are consistent with attainment and maintenance of acceptable air quality.

Research

Research needs to consider the limitations and capabilities of current model sets in light of the need to assess current urban issues. Where the current models are lacking, new model structures need to be developed. Specifically, the new models need to be able to address the following issues:

• How do transportation capacity improvements affect the level and pattern of trip making in a corridor or metropolitan region?
• Under what circumstances and to what extent are the benefits of capacity improvements offset by additional trip making? Under what circumstances and to what extent are speed-related benefits offset because of changes in mode choice and destination choice?
• How sensitive are land uses and development patterns to im-

provements in transportation capacity? How and to what extent are changes in household and business location associated with investments in transportation capacity? Under what conditions and over what time period would such changes occur?

This research needs to distinguish various types of transit and highway improvements as well as to relate the assessments to socioeconomic and physical characteristics of the urban/metropolitan area and region for a sample of representative regions.

Management and Coordination of Scale and Data

Problem

Transportation planners' quest for a regional focus for their models that could capture both ends of 90 to 95 percent of all travel has required geographic compromises. All travel is assumed to emanate at the center of an often arbitrarily defined zone and to travel to the centers of other arbitrarily defined zones. The total number of these zones has had major impacts on the computer space and time required to handle the routing of this travel over the network. This has tended to keep zone systems small in number and coarse in scale.

The size of zones also is critical. Intrazonal travel is lost and the bias of zone centroid loading on route assignment is a major factor in the high error levels associated with estimates of traffic volumes on surface facilities, especially arterials and collectors with at-grade intersections.

The crudeness in the planning process has not been limited to geography. The representation of the transportation network itself has suffered not only from the sparseness of the routes included but also from the "impoverished" description of network attributes. The lack of data regarding intersection signal control, phasing, geometrics, turn restrictions, turn bays, etc. has required the transportation planner to settle for capacities that are not link- or intersection-specific. Compound this with 24-hr assignments that are factored down to represent peak periods, and the coarseness of the procedures is accentuated even further.

Land use inventories for a region or residential population and employment at place of work are also packaged in zone systems. To integrate land use data into the transportation models often requires a reconciliation of two separate zone systems with some mechanical introduction of error. To forecast future land use and trip end data requires further "jiggling" of areal systems.

In addition, the appropriate scale of the geographic partitioning may vary according to the study or problem in question. The closer the trip origin or destination is to a specific facility, the more significant is zone size. If two, three, four, or more facilities pass through the zone, on which facility should the trip enter or leave the zone? Thus, a separate zone, and incidentally, a separate network, is dictated by the very geographic nature of the problem.

To cope with such issues, hierarchical zone and network systems were devised in the 1970s to deal with the variations in zone and network scale and data associated with different problems. But coping with the parallel data requirements from the land use settlement patterns does not yield easily. Yet even with perfect trip generation, distribution, and mode split models, a mismatch or incompatibility of geography can impair, distort, or even destroy the travel estimation and assignment validity and consequences of a particular land use scenario.

Need

In preparation for the 1990 census, the Census Bureau had all of the census block boundaries or all of the U.S. Geographical Service "quad" maps for each of the counties in the United States and territories digitized, and where 1980 Dual Independent Map Encoding file address systems existed, they were integrated. These digitized block boundaries or segments are available under the Topologically Integrated Geographic Encoding and Referencing (TIGER) files from the Census Bureau. These files will permit the introduction of fine-scaled (block level) data into transportation and regional planning. These segments and blocks could represent a fine-grained data base that could be aggregated to any number of alternative zone systems and that simultaneously aggregates the data available at the block level. This requires geographic information systems (GIS) soft-ware to accomplish. The data are limited only by the data entered into the data base.

In addition to TIGER, all kinds of secondary data abound: tax parcel data, utility data, automobile registration addresses, accidents, crime statistics, structures, zoning, population, density, and the elements of the 1990 census data (including the journey-to-work data) when they become available.

The union of the TIGER files, a data base structure (which could be the census block), a land use data set, a transportation model software system, and a GIS system to manage and integrate data of the right kind (qualitative) at the right scale could produce the traffic requirements of a particular settlement pattern and transport system and the impacts of that traffic in terms of evaluation criteria, including at least

- Safety (accident cost),
- Environment,
- Travel time,
- Travel cost,
- Historic structures and places,
- Energy consumption, and
- Air quality (a special case of the environment).

This capability could be used in a practical mode to test and evaluate specific transportation improvements or policies including traffic engineering, transportation system management, TDM, and changes in the settlement patterns of the region. It could also be used as a research facility to test alternative approaches to transportation planning, city planning, or both. And if or when a model that could represent the interaction of transportation and land use including settlement shifts in response to transportation changes (physical or policy) is available and integrated into this system, a research facility for seeking joint land use-transportation solutions could be available.

Because of the flexibility of scale, this approach could handle problems at different scales ranging from neighborhood design issues to regional thoroughfare analyses. With two or several such facilities in operation, data and answers could be generated for purposes of assisting in formulation of federal policy.

Research

Two or more transport-land use research centers should be sponsored. These centers would build on previous experience in both transport and land use planning, use state-of-the-art computational facilities, TIGER files, GIS software, and other data base files, and seek answers to real transportation-land use issues in their region. These facilities would also be research and training centers.

Urban Freight Movement

Problem

Freight considerations are not now generally taken into account in planning or policy decisions on urban land use-transportation effects, except in specific local cases such as port development. Much of the current understanding of the linkage among freight movement, terminal location, and transportation is based upon intuition, conjecture, or observation. Few cities or regions explicitly consider freight needs in transportation planning.

Need

Because the costs of moving goods within urban areas are comparable with the costs of moving people, and because freight considerations affect industrial and terminal location decisions, it is important to include freight in the overall study of transportation, urban form, and the environment. Better understanding of the linkages between freight, freight terminals, industrial location, and transportation (intraurban, interurban, and international) and the effects of such linkages could lead to more informed decisions in the following areas:

• Land use policies that encouraged grouping of industry on the basis of complementary trade, thereby lowering freight costs and reducing truck VMT by facilitating backhauls;
• Land use zoning practices that reduced freight demands by encouraging a mix of complementary activities within a site or in close proximity to each other instead of separating various activities (heavy industry, light industry, processing, warehousing, retail, freight terminals, residential);
• Policies that allowed freight terminals consolidating freight from several shippers to locate near to their customers and did not force them into remote locations;
• Decisions about zoning of land for industrial, commercial, and transport purposes that gave consideration to access to transport infrastructure (especially location close to freeways and arterial roads to minimize VMT on lower-order roads);
• Location of intercity road freight terminals on the urban fringe to reduce the need for larger line haul trucks to penetrate the urban area;
• Encouragement of large shippers to have direct access to rail

freight services (e.g., on-dock or near-dock intermodal container transfer facilities at or near seaports);

• Industrial location policies that favored goods movement (e.g., truck routes, access restrictions, site design);

• Use of investment or management of freight facilities (road investment, terminals, ports, airports, etc.) as a tool to help shape urban form;

• Large-scale urban renewal at higher residential and job densities to take advantage of the presence in many cities of freight terminal activities (particularly rail, but sometimes maritime) on large areas of land near the central city; and

• Policies that affect the cost of transportation of goods to both domestic markets and international markets, both of which require the presence of an efficient freight system (road, rail, sea, air) and quality modal interchange facilities, and thus the economic viability of industries (including the number of jobs, the tax base, etc.).

Research

Research needs to be conducted to establish the strength of these issues and relationships, quantifying them when possible and recognizing that other factors and trade-offs are involved. Freight can affect policy in a number of areas. The effectiveness of alternative strategies (e.g., regulation, enforcement, investment, traffic management, industrial location) needs to be assessed, because there may be alternative ways of achieving freight-related goals.

Methodology might include

• Economic models (e.g., transportation and regional economic viability);

• Location models (e.g., industrial location to and within cities);

• Case studies (e.g., urban redevelopment);

• Monitoring (e.g., effect of truck restriction policies on fleet composition, truck use, shippers, and receivers);

• Transport modeling (e.g., effects of location on truck VMT);

• Impact modeling (e.g., noise, emissions, safety, intrusion); and

• Practices (e.g., inclusion of freight in transportation and land use planning processes).

Research results would be implemented through such means as

changes to zoning ordinances, changes to building regulations, traffic management, environmental legislation (especially noise and emissions), and perhaps the priorities given to various transport infrastructure proposals (e.g., access roads serving port areas).

Impact of New Highway Technologies

Problem

New technologies, including the numerous technologies being considered under the rubric of IVHS, could drastically alter travel patterns, locational advantages and disadvantages, and ultimately the shape and size of metropolitan areas and metropolitan and regional systems. Potential capacity increases resulting from IVHS applications could substantially alter land development opportunities in the corridors where the technologies are applied.

Need

Research is needed to explore the possible impacts of near-term technological options (e.g., route guidance and devices that could substantially reduce accident-related capacity decreases such as lane centering, automated braking, and accident removal). Longer-term possibilities such as automated highways providing high-speed, very high capacity travel (but perhaps only on a few facilities and with limited access and egress) also need to be examined.

Research

Research on this topic would require postulation of alternative technology formats and deployments. Work could proceed from there either using analytic approaches or applying real transportation and land use data from selected cities or regions. The interaction of the technologies with such data as land markets, development decision making, and local government regulatory approaches could be considered in some detail.

SUMMARY

The recommendations made reflect concerns about the impacts of rapid growth and development in the 1980s. These impacts were focused largely in the suburban areas of the nation, as the demographic "bubble" of baby-boomers entered the labor force, purchased houses, and fueled the economy. The decade saw a tremendous increase in two-worker households and in automobile ownership and use. These demographic factors will change over the next two decades, resulting in a further change in research needs. As these issues are dealt with, three basic choices are available:

• Try to slow development or direct development to where adequate public facilities exist or can be provided.
• Go back to older solutions such as higher densities of development and greater use of public transportation. This could include structuring development into more environmentally responsible forms, including balancing housing and employment by area.
• Go forward by pricing mobility properly and introducing high-technology approaches to increase capacity or manage demand.

All three will probably be needed in the right places at the right time if the balance among land use, transportation, and the environment is to be addressed within fiscal and other constraints.

In any case, money, time, skills, and, above all, agreement on solutions will be necessary.

Workshop 3

CHAIR: **Sheldon M. Edner**
SECRETARY: **Thomas G. Coleman**
PARTICIPANTS: **Daniel Brand, G. Bruce Douglas III, Robert T. Dunphy, Kathy Gerwig, Genevieve Guiliano, Jerry B. Schneider, Sam Seskin**

Workshop 3 produced a set of questions concerning the four basic charges posed by the conference organizers. These questions reflected the consensus of the group that the relationship between transportation and urban form was, at best, still ambiguous in many respects. Although some elements of this relationship are understood, the overall cause and effect connection between transportation systems and behavior and the structure of urban development and change still defies definitive specification. Hence, many of the issues raised subsequently reflect not only the need to specify specific impacts (e.g., congestion relief), but also systemic forces on the level of the relative impact of transportation systems changes on shifts in development.

BASIC UNDERSTANDING

Decision Making

The decision making system operates at several different levels. At the macro level, the institutional structures and responsibilities are decentralized and diffuse. Further, in the past decade significant change has occurred, occasioned by federal policy initiatives that have shifted many of the institutional loci of decision making. In response to federal policy changes, states have assumed greater responsibility for financing transportation improvements and, at the same time, downloaded responsibilities to local decision makers. The role of metropolitan planning organizations (MPOs), in particular, has changed markedly, reflecting changing financial conditions and the elimination of their A-95 Clearinghouse role in many areas.

Although the regional transportation dimension of their planning function remains intact, changes in many other policy areas have forced them to revamp and reorder their institutional role. As a result, they have a much more diverse capacity across the nation.

Institutional shifts have occurred in other respects as a result of emerging new agency players in the urban context. New providers, both in service and form, have appeared in many areas. Coupled with the shifting state and local roles, this has further decentralized and complicated the overall institutional picture in terms of transportation and the nature of institutional decision making across all dimensions of urban development.

At a planning level, the processes of planning transportation systems continue to reflect a number of problems. The integration of highway and public transportation planning processes—not to mention the linkage between transportation and land use planning—is problematic. Information bases, planning horizons, procedural mechanisms, and basic assumptions about the relative relationship between land use and infrastructure development reflect very different assumptions and processes.

Further complicating this picture is the emergence of several new policy initiatives that have altered basic conceptual arrangements among policy arenas. The Americans with Disabilities Act, Clean Air Act Amendments, 1990 Budget Act, and emerging issues in wetlands are creating fundamental realignments in planning relationships.

The overall impact is to create a state of turbulence in the institutional and procedural context of transportation decision making. Consequently, the perceived need to revisit fundamental knowledge federal, concerning state, and local decision systems and processes can be reflected by the following questions:

- How is the decision making for capital improvement programs and transportation improvement programs by different groups with different objectives related?
- Are decision systems transferable? Can a set of good or bad models for decision making or an inventory of institutional forms be identified?
- Is it possible to draw from international examples (i.e., replicate Colcord studies of the 1970s)?

- What is the impact of single-issue regulatory bodies on transportation decision making?
- How can the impact of mixed institutional operating and construction authority, ownership, regulatory, and finance responsibilities be understood and improved?
- What rural versus urban trade-offs are necessary to foster new governance structures for regional areas?
- Is there a model content for regional plans and processes of planning? How are integration and consistency of local and regional plans achieved? What is the need for appropriate staffing resources and regulatory power?
- How can the exurban and urban population within a region be integrated and educated? Can regional boundaries be aligned with an inherent constituency?
- What regulatory policies are needed to reinforce land use regulations?

Financing

- How can better identification of benefit streams for private investment return be achieved?
- What are the limits to private participation?
- How can areas of pent-up demand (under investment) be identified?
- Which technical and analytical methods will better support analysis of financing options?
- How can the limits of public-private negotiation be better understood?
- Are there more effective ways for involving the private sector in public decisions and options?
- How can public benefits from private projects be quantified to allow better assessment of costs?
- How can alternative financing horizons be understood?
- How can the regionwide benefits of transportation investment be better identified?
- How can the politics of what will "sell" be understood?

Housing and Jobs

- Are there net economic benefits from transportation investments?
- How can the redistribution of existing development versus attracting new growth be understood?

- Are noneconomic benefits sufficient to support economically marginal projects?
- How important are transportation factors in personal location decisions?
- How do developers understand location preferences and market data?
- Are market factors alone sufficient to model landowner sales?
- How can submarkets within urban areas be identified and modeled?
- How can the "starter" home market be understood?
- How can employer factors in employment location decisions be better understood?
- How can appropriate public policies be identified to support a balance of jobs and housing?
- Should new town studies in the United States, Britain, and France be updated?

Urban Design

- What are the drawbacks of reduced parking?
- What is the marketability of development that reduces parking and travel?
- Should suburban activity centers mimic central business districts (CBDs)?
- Is there an appropriate diversity of activities for suburban activity centers?
- What is the effect of density thresholds (i.e., reducing automobile use in suburban activity centers)?
- What are the mechanisms for integrating transit stations in suburban activity centers? How can they be sold to developers?
- Does transit-oriented design work? Do density floors and parking lids encourage transit use?

Options

- What is the time horizon for linkage between transportation and urban form to take effect?
- What is the effect of real-time information on transportation and location decisions?
- How does the extent of work force decentralization from technology introduction lead to possible trip length reduction?

- What are the private and social costs of existing transportation alternatives?
- Is there a land use equivalent of traveler information systems? Can location decisions be optimized?
- What is the impact of supply and level-of-service uncertainty on trip travel behavior?

Environment and Energy

- What are the total social costs (subsidized travel, congestion, environment, new users) of transportation options?
- Can changes in life-style and vehicle necessary to make environmental changes be sold?
- Are technological fixes alone enough?
- Can the impediments to market-based strategies to promote efficiency be identified?
- What are the effects on the environment of transportation improvements?

METHODOLOGY

The panel recognized a substantial need to reexamine basic approaches to the development and analysis of data in the context of transportation. Basic tools, such as the ASCE trip generation data, were felt to be obsolete in terms of useful application to the analysis of travel behavior and development patterns. Demographic patterns and life-style shifts have created new dynamic forces underlying the overall development of urban areas. More important, basic benchmarks against which to measure change and guide development are lacking. There is little clarity or specification to the anticipated goals. If planning and transportation system development are going to avoid a fundamentally reactive role in the development of urban form, there may need to be some definition and stipulation of desired urban form context.

Decision Making

- Is the type of urban form desired in 30 years known?
- Are there alternative images of urban form that should be attempted?
- Do the methodological and conceptual tools exist to understand

behavior in terms of (a) life-style, (b) class, (c) demographics, and (d) economics?

• Given an adequate knowledge of travel behavior, how can incentives be designed to shape transportation choices?

• Can individual behavior be connected with socially desired outcomes?

• Can the real effect of options (e.g., congestion pricing) on transportation outcomes be perceived?

• Are there alternatives to social experimentation?

• Does travel between activity centers exist?

• Can a paradigm of intracity, intercity, rural, and tourism markets be developed?

• Can case studies of policy options be used to demonstrate real effects? Change over time? Trends?

• Can urban form be measured or cities classified on the basis of population density and economic activity?

• What are the impacts of incomplete plan implementation?

• How can transportation be thought of in other than modal terms? System terms? How can it be integrated across modal approaches?

• How can a conceptual framework be created in a quasi-economic way to understand social outcomes so that "what if" alternatives can be done?

• Can land use patterns be integrated in the planning process?

• How can user demand be connected with the planning process?

• Is demand shaped or responded to?

• Does knowledge exist to "fix" the imperfect transportation market?

• Are cities addressed differently in terms of growth, no growth, and recycling?

• Can optimal city locations be identified and enhanced?

• How are nontransport and "local" issues related to?

• How are accessibility and mobility (size and distance; jobs/time or consumers) measured?

• Is there an optimal improvement in transportation?

• From a federal perspective, should investment take place and to what extent? How should research support investment strategies?

• How can the existing transportation system be made better?

• Can transportation and land use benefits be measured? What are they? What are the productivity paybacks locally and nationally?

• Is there a comparable measurement strategy for costs that links them to benefits more effectively than current strategies? Can noneconomic costs and benefits be included?

- What can be learned from careful analysis of case studies of hard community decisions?
- Should more before-and-after studies be conducted (particularly of highway improvements)?
- Are case studies of decision making concerning locally funded projects valuable? Can the factors that allowed the development of consensus be identified?
- How does one synthesize across case studies for generalizable factors?
- Why are highways underdesigned and transit systems over-designed? Is this a failure of the planning process?
- Are there small-scale investments to improve system performance?
- Are the cross-elasticities between transit and highways vis-à-vis design versus behavior really understood?
- How can scenario building methods be used to inform "what if" decision making? Can present time versus future outcomes be incorporated? Are there models that can do this?
- How does people's behavior change in response to policy changes (e.g., compression and travel changes resulting from a compressed work week)?
- Can better cross-modal elasticity studies be developed along the lines of those done in San Francisco and New York?
- How do suburban activity centers function in terms of travel? Can "contact" studies be used to assess this? What kind of contact (e.g., telephone and fax contacts) would be measured?
- Can the potential for further multinucleation be measured from an economic perspective?
- How are business dispersion patterns evaluated across activity centers? How much of this is real growth versus reallocation?
- Can the travel impacts on nonactivity center businesses be measured? Does a useful concept of activity centers exist?
- Can information be obtained to support the feasibility of design options that rely on pedestrian and transit alternatives?
- Can the feasibility of parking management be assessed? Does a real inventory of available parking exist?
- Can strategies be designed to encourage more efficient pricing (i.e., increase high-density buildout)?
- What is the future of existing shopping malls in terms of the impact of catalog shopping and other factors?
- Can prototypical metropolitan areas be identified for large-scale studies across a number of factors? Will this facilitate analysis?

- Can the ability to model theories in land use be improved (especially those that incorporate a feedback component)? Can these include some international comparison factors?
- Is there a predictive model of household location decision making? Should surveys and focus groups be used to help understand the value of travel in residential choice?
- Can studies of trip length versus opportunity trip length (i.e., the impact of living closer to work in terms of other trips generated) be updated?
- How can transport information be visualized to help aid public thinking about transportation options?
- Can global positioning information be used effectively for analysis?
- What is the relationship between intelligent vehicle/highway system technology and modeling capacity? Will the models become obsolete?
- Are there interactive tools (i.e., computers for testing pricing alternatives) for decision makers?
- Can technology forecasting and impact assessment be done given the speed of change?
- Can an understanding be developed of citizen willingness to pay for improvements versus the perception of congestion?
- What is the impact of the proliferation of smaller employers and impact on dispersion and travel patterns?
- Does the size of the employer affect worker residential decisions?
- Does the ability exist to measure the air quality impacts of transportation projects (most notably in the case of the automobile)?

POLICY AND INSTITUTIONS

The issues surrounding policy and institutional options are a direct reflection of the ambiguity inherent in the linkage between transportation and urban form. At one level the changing context of transportation systems, operating conditions, planning processes, and policy content has created a great deal of ambiguity concerning the future of urban development. Concomitantly, the general arena of public decision making and land use directions has also witnessed substantial stress and change. As a result, linking outcomes to decisions is difficult to track and attribute.

Indeed, the policy arena has become exceedingly more complex. Regulatory options have increased. The location of appropriate policy and decision making responsibility is ambiguous. The linkage between policy decisions across policy arenas (e.g., Clean Air Act Amendments) has led to modified procedures and agendas not rooted in pure transportation objectives. Financing arrangements are currently on a roller coaster of diversification and change, particularly as reauthorization of the Surface Transportation Act proceeds. Finally, there are significant impacts arising from noninstitutional issues (e.g., the graying of the transportation work force and shifting technology) that are also placing increasing burdens on the transportation policymaking machinery.

As a consequence, there is a real need to establish a broad framework within which to couch necessary decisions. The workshop participants believe that the new National Transportation Policy is a step in this direction.

Policy-related questions include the following:

- What should be the content of a regional transportation plan?
- What should the process look like? What should be the role of the federal government in specifying expectations and in terms of financing or professional standards?
- What is the role of the National Transportation Policy and Plan?
- Should a high-quality demonstration program with specific objectives be established?
- Should the federal government specify performance standards rather than process?
- Has alterative analysis produced better decisions? Can non-transportation alternatives be incorporated?
- How are incentives created that will lead to better projects?
- What incentives can be used to encourage cross-modal decision making?
- Can design and performance and standards be made flexible in specification and implementation?
- What options are available for expanding the state role in land use planning? Should the federal government provide leadership to states?
- Do transport capacity improvements generate unconsidered environmental impacts? What should be the process of resolving conflicts between programs?
- What are the transportation policy implications of the Clean Air Act Amendments?

- What are the institutional implications of the interaction between air quality and transportation in planning and regulation?
- Should the issue of federal tax policy be revisited with regard to optimal transportation and land use polices?
- Should fund allocation for programs be based more heavily on formula factors (i.e., should discretionary programs be avoided)?
- How can university programs in transportation planning and urban form be encouraged?
- How can federal personnel policies be modified to encourage greater disciplinary diversity in hiring?

RESEARCH RECOMMENDATIONS

From among the wide range of issues suggested, the workshop participants determined that the following constitute the most immediate and important issues in terms of the transportation and urban form research agenda. They are not listed in priority order.

Transportation and Land Use

- The role of transportation in personal location decision making.
- Trends in CBD/suburban areas regarding development patterns, taking into account jobs, demography, and so forth.
- Impacts on business and business decisions of transportation demand management (TDM) policies.
- The manner in which transportation investment decisions are made, with full cognizance of costs and benefits.
- Assessment of noncapital transportation options in terms of their contribution vis-à-vis capital options, location choice patterns by employers, and policy institution and decision making.
- Identification of incentives that lead decision makers to more effective and desirable decisions.
- Analysis of decision systems (elements of successful consensus processes) using case studies.
- Voter support for financing mechanisms under alternative transportation contexts.
- Mechanisms for resolving transportation-air quality conflicts in program and plan implementation.
- Listing of available policy instruments available and assessment of their relative payoffs and utilities.

- Review and assessment of benchmarks of successful transport improvements and their relationship to policy options.
- Examination of values of individual decision makers and their role in the decision process using a cross-comparison of public-private decisions.

Travel Behavior Response

- Demonstration of congestion pricing in an area where it has already been modeled.
- Examination of behavioral response impacts on transportation network, social system, and business TDM employment (trip reduction in response to TDM strategies).

Tool Kit

Basic technical information needs include:

- Models of transport-air quality relationships.
- Interactive models for decision makers.
- Updated data on travel patterns, system performance, and trip generation.
- Revision of before-and-after analyses using longitudinal studies.
- Evaluation of household location choice related to changing household characteristics and career patterns.
- Travel time budgets under congestion conditions across all trips.
- Price elasticity studies for parking and congestion pricing.

Workshop 4

CHAIR: **Martin Wachs**
SECRETARY: **Patrick DeCorla-Souza**
PARTICIPANTS: **Keith Bartholomew, Paul N. Bay, John R. Borchert, Norman M. Glasgow, Jr., Robert Joseph, H. Pike Oliver, Richard H. Pratt, Stephen H. Putman, Edward Weiner, Linda Wilshusen**

Workshop 4 participants began deliberations by addressing the relationships between air quality and transportation, land use and transportation, and density and social and environmental objectives.

AIR QUALITY AND TRANSPORTATION

The group believed that more information and better models are needed to assess whether building new highway capacity will, in the long term, improve air quality or harm it. What is the relationship between available capacity and growth? If capacity increases are limited to "stress points" (i.e., bottleneck locations), will they still be perceived as new capacity and result in increased development? Research in modeling the relationships of transportation investments, land use, travel demand, and air quality would help the relationships to be understood and would help better policy decisions to be made.

LAND USE AND TRANSPORTATION

There was much concern about the ability of currently available models to forecast the impacts of transportation investments on land use decisions. Some urban areas that have experimented with such models (such as the PLUM model developed by the Association of Bay Area Governments) found that they could not provide the needed answers. It was pointed out that the time dimension is not as well

168

understood as it should be. The collective understanding of the dynamics of the relationship between transportation investments and land use decisions must be improved, as must that of the ways in which factors other than accessibility (e.g., economic, social, and institutional factors) affect the timing of land development decisions. In addition, a better understanding is needed of the "secondary" or unintended land use responses to increases in transportation capacity.

Currently, UMTA's guidelines on alternatives analysis do not permit explicit recognition of the changes in land use development characteristics that result from different types of transportation investments (i.e., land use must be kept constant for all alternatives analyzed). Better models of the interactions between transportation and land use would allow more realistic analyses to be conducted.

DENSITY AND SOCIAL AND ENVIRONMENTAL OBJECTIVES

There was a general consensus that research should seek to improve understanding of the causes and effects of urban sprawl. New homes are being built at low densities on the fringes of urban areas, whereas redevelopment in the inner city is ignored. Several questions that might lead to research were raised:

• What are the future costs of these current development decisions? Would nonpolluting cars and energy-efficient vehicles change negative views about suburban sprawl?

• Do people reject high densities because of race and class associations or because they inherently dislike high-density environments?

• What are the effects of high-density development on the economy and the environment?

• How can it be ensured that the high densities needed to make transit work will be brought about after investments are made in transit infrastructure?

SUGGESTED RESEARCH

To throw light on these issues, several research projects were suggested:

• An update of the discredited 1970s research contained in *The*

Costs of Sprawl (1) that would overcome its deficiencies and would include identification and quantification of the full social costs and benefits of low-density development vis-à-vis moderate and high-density development. Costs to be quantified should include those relating to air quality; energy; infrastructure; soft services such as police and fire protection; parks and open spaces; loss of agricultural land, wetlands, and endangered species; and global warming.

• An evaluation of methods to "charge back" the social costs of suburban development to those responsible for the costs.

• An evaluation of the long-term impacts on both the economy and the environment of achieving higher densities and encouraging congestion. The evaluation would include questions such as, "What would have happened if freeways had not been built within urban areas?" Comparative studies of foreign cities, such as those done by Newman and Kenworthy (2) and by Pucher (3, 4) were recommended. A comparison of Brisbane, Australia (which has no freeways), and Atlanta, Georgia, was suggested.

• Case studies of urban areas in which incentives and disincentives or mandates for high-density development have worked with the objective of developing guidance for policymakers on how to ensure that land use development decisions are consistent with transit development decisions.

• Survey research to identify consumer preferences and answer questions such as, "Does the market present consumers with sufficient choices for high-density living environments?" If the market is not responding to consumer preferences, why not?" "What are the living and travel preferences of diverse new immigrant groups (e.g., single-parent and childless families, the elderly, and other market segments that have emerged more recently)?" "How can high-density living be made more appealing to a large number of Americans?"

NEW TECHNOLOGY OPTIONS

The consensus was that there is a lack of understanding of several issues relating to the impact of new technology. Among the questions that may provide the focus for research, the following were mentioned:

• How extensive is telecommuting at the national level? What is its upper limit?

- What are the effects of telecommuting and telecommunications on travel and urban form? For example, will they lead to increased long-distance travel, just as the invention and use of the telephone may have increased the need for interpersonal interaction? What has the impact of faxing been with respect to trip reduction? Will telecommuting merely shift travel to different times of the day (i.e., will workers use telecommuting only to work at home during peak travel periods and travel to or from work during off-peak periods)?
- What are the potential benefits of information-based intelligent vehicle/highway system (IVHS) technology with respect to highway speed, capacity, and reliability of travel? What will the impacts be on roads providing access to freeways with enhanced capacity?

In the view of some participants, the forms of IVHS that involve direct vehicle control through the highway will not be implemented in the foreseeable future because of financial limitations and liability questions. On the other hand, the group felt that some applications of IVHS were much more promising, especially those that would lead to marginal changes in the use of existing highway capacity through transportation system management and transportation demand management (TDM). For example, IVHS applications that increased priority for transit vehicles and vanpools were deemed more likely to be adopted in the nearer-term future.

To answer such questions, new types of data collection strategies will be needed. For example, surveys will have to be designed to find out what trips were not made as a result of communications technology improvements, as well as what trips were.

On a related subject, the group felt that it is not fully understood why nonwork trips are increasing faster than work trips as a proportion of total travel. Many interesting theories were offered, and it was thought that the phenomenon should be a subject of more systematic research.

TRANSPORTATION PRICING

The group was surprisingly unanimous in agreeing that congestion pricing is an idea whose time has come. Some questions that should be researched are the following:

- What changes in law may be needed to govern how revenues may be used?

- What is the relationship between congestion and the underpricing of roads and housing? To what extent is congestion simply the result of not charging road users or suburban residents the costs for new infrastructure made necessary by their actions?
- Who benefits from new suburban developments and who bears the costs? Costs for congestion pricing or impact fees will be borne primarily by younger people. There may be a "moral" question here—are costs being passed on unfairly to future generations?

It was suggested that a major demonstration project be initiated to study the legal and other institutional barriers that might stand in the way of the implementation of congestion pricing on a larger scale.

Parking management, it was thought, is a more feasible means of achieving some of the goals that are often set for congestion pricing. Several questions relating to parking management need to be researched:

- What are the behavioral implications of parking availability and cost? In the Portland, Oregon, CBD, it was stated, the institution of a parking ceiling of one space per 1,000 ft^2 resulted in a 50 percent transit mode share for work trips to the CBD (5).
- How can tax law changes be used to provide employers with incentives or disincentives to reduce the inducement to drive alone that free parking currently provides? An example provided was a requirement that employers give employees the option of receiving cash in lieu of free parking.
- When parking ceilings are instituted for existing developments, how can the surplus spaces be turned into usable "infill" development? What are the nontransportation constraints to infill development (e.g., sewer system capacity)?

It was suggested that this conference be directed to incorporate work done by participants of a Parking Management Symposium sponsored by the Association for Commuter Transportation (5).

Concerns were expressed that the ITE *Trip Generation Manual* (6) provides trip rates that do not reflect the difference that parking price and availability can make with respect to trip reduction. Nor do the ITE trip generation rates reflect variations caused by such variables as transit availability, urban location, region of the country, development size, and so on. The manual should be replaced with a much more sophisticated product, possibly a computer package in the form of an expert system.

NEOTRADITIONAL DESIGN

Neotraditional design was the name that was used by workshop participants for the recent emphasis on livable streets, including mixed-use development; emphasis on pedestrian, transit, and bicycle circulation systems; and automobile-free zones. The group determined that community-scale neotraditional design raises several questions that need to be answered:

• How can neotraditional design be accommodated within the hierarchy of highway functional classes to assure that regional through traffic is served adequately and safely?
• How can existing development be retrofitted to allow such land uses as shopping, daycare, and recreation within walking distance of residences?
• How effective are such design concepts within a "functioning" urban area? (Most have been implemented in isolated environments.)

It was suggested that projects that have been implemented should be monitored more systematically than they have been and that the U.S. Department of Transportation could sponsor the publication of a handbook of community design guidelines that would reflect a balance between community objectives and regional traffic management objectives.

SUBURBAN ACTIVITY CENTERS

A Conference on Traffic Congestion and Suburban Activity Centers was held in 1989 (7). An important issue raised by that conference was, "What is the optimum design of the suburban activity center to maximize the effectiveness of transportation demand management actions?" The design would consider land use mix, density, and development size as well as parking cost and availability and access by all modes, including transit, bicycle, pedestrian, and high-occupancy vehicle (HOV).

The group decided that the "optimum design" research be done not just for new centers but also with a view toward retrofitting existing centers. Such research should determine how existing large housing developments can be retrofitted with shops and services and how existing shopping centers can be retrofitted with offices and housing.

It was also suggested that the "optimum design" should consider possible synergistic effects when several different regional centers are interconnected by networks of superior transit or HOV facilities. Optimum design of such combinations of activity center and regional network and their effects on travel demand could also be a subject for research.

HOUSING AND JOBS

The group agreed that the lack of affordable housing within reasonable commuting range of jobs leads to long work trip lengths. The discussion quickly turned to how balance can be restored between jobs and housing. Questions that might lead to research were the following:

• Will market forces automatically restore balance as employers move out to their labor markets?
• Will high-speed rail lead to greater imbalance, because it will allow longer work trips to be made?
• How are the fiscal disparities that lead to jobs-housing imbalance overcome? How can political jurisdictions be kept from competing with one another to attract employers while at the same time zoning out low-income housing from their jurisdictions?
• What are the basic regional boundaries and community-scale commuter sheds for which planning should be done? (Political boundaries are artificial and inadequate for assessing whether jobs and housing are "in balance".)
• What would be the effects of different types of regional institutional structure and tax-base sharing?
• What would it take to get support from local elected officials for regional government?

It was suggested that comparative case studies be done of different types of regional governmental structure and the development patterns that have resulted. Hypothetical studies should then be conducted to estimate the effects that alternative forms of regional tax-base sharing could have in urban areas that do not have such arrangements. Finally, the findings of the studies should be disseminated widely to local elected officials in order to promote tax-base sharing. It was suggested that the dissemination be in the form of videotapes or brief information packets to ensure that busy decision makers would see the results.

FINANCING AND DECISION MAKING

Financing and decision making issues relating to transportation and land use had been discussed previously by the group under other topics. The only new issues raised by the group related to the need for a goal-based system to allocate funding for transportation and environment-related projects, instead of the existing categorical grants. The following questions that might lead to research were raised:

- Do good examples of goal-based allocation systems in use exist, and what are their effects on allocation of resources?
- How would a goal-based system affect allocation of resources? (A demonstration project, with federal incentives, was suggested.)
- How can constituencies be built for a goal-based system? (The U.S. Department of Transportation has found it difficult to get urban block grants legislated by Congress because of a lack of support from both transit and highway interest groups.)

It was again emphasized that all research must be linked to the dissemination of information.

METHODOLOGIES

Research to improve analysis tools was recommended in several areas:

- A much more sophisticated product—perhaps a menu-driven expert system—should be developed to enhance policy analysis of trip rates because the ITE *Trip Generation Manual* (6) provides no help to analysts in estimating the impacts of policy changes such as changes in parking price and availability.
- A catalog and compilation in more usable form (e.g., a set of handbooks that are updated regularly) should be made of what is already known.
- Methods to quantify non-point-source pollution (both air and water pollution) should be developed, as should methods to mitigate

the pollution's effects.   Air pollutants from aviation should be addressed.

• Forecasts of air pollutant concentrations should be improved. (The level of accuracy of models that predict concentrations is much lower than that of models that predict emissions.)

• Survey research to improve understanding of methods to change human behavior should be supported.   (Changes in attitudes about recycling over the past 10 years show that it is possible to change human behavior.)

The importance of technology transfer and dissemination of research results was reiterated.   Some ways to improve dissemination were suggested:

• Past attempts at dissemination should be evaluated to learn what improvements can be made.

• Information produced from models should be simplified to make it more usable.   Users such as lawyers should be educated in the use of model results.

• Work should be done with organizations that provide information to decision makers.

• A bridge to the public should be established.

• Better ways to manage research should be sought through systematic, ongoing efforts to summarize, synthesize, and understand research results and to find out where gaps in knowledge exist.

• A standard set of handbooks [e.g., the *Highway Capacity Manual* (*8*)] should be established that would be updated on a regular basis and to which the analyst could turn for the best and most recent information.

POLICY AND INSTITUTIONS

Policy and institutional research questions had been discussed previously under other topics.   New issues that surfaced included the misuse of level of service (LOS) on highways as a criterion for measuring transportation system performance and the need to develop alternative criteria; mechanisms to preserve utility easement right-of-way; and the overcoming of barriers to implementation of policy changes.

Level-of-Service Measures

The use of the LOS criterion in system evaluation can lead to wrong policy decisions, because it does not provide information about nonautomobile modes (transit, bicycling, walking) and HOVs. Congestion itself may not be bad, and may in fact be necessary for success of TDM strategies. The LOS criterion should therefore be replaced with a criterion or set of criteria that addresses all modes, environmental objectives, and urban form issues. The criteria should measure person mobility rather than vehicle mobility, and should include standardized consideration of performance with respect to environmental, social, and economic efficiency objectives.

Right-of-Way Preservation

Utility easements are being lost to development, and institutional mechanisms (such as those for rail lines) do not exist to encourage their preservation. The rights-of-way of power lines, for example, should be preserved for use by transportation modes that may have not been developed yet. Work in this area should develop legislation to preserve right-of-way (e.g., provision of first right of refusal for public agencies) and provide financial resources for purchase of rights-of-way.

Policy Implementation

Although research relating to analytical tools will provide the information on policy effects needed by decision makers, implementation of these policies will involve understanding the barriers to implementation and methods to overcome these barriers. For example, people are afraid to change, and their fears of the unknown can be a major constraint to making policy changes. It is therefore necessary to devise effective methods for public education and citizen participation to enhance the likelihood of public acceptance.

RESEARCH PRIORITIES

The group's priorities are presented in the order discussed. No attempt was made to order the priorities from highest to lowest. The issues and details of each research priority were presented in previous sections, and the reader is referred to those sections for additional background information.

Tax-Base Sharing and Regional Government

It was thought that the revenue sharing and regional governance issue is fundamental to decision making. Priority research should include

- A series of case studies to identify where and how financial considerations are causing irrational distribution of housing and jobs. (States and urban areas that have found institutional solutions should be identified and studied.)
- A study of the potential impacts of alternative solutions in the Los Angeles basin.
- A demonstration project that would provide financial incentives to test solutions within a region.
- Evaluation of various forms of regional government—metropolitan planning organizations, special purpose districts, and so on—to assess their effectiveness and how the federal interest could be served better at the regional level.

Data Collection

Good data are needed for modeling to better describe the nature of the problem. Smaller urban areas that are growing rapidly should not be ignored. New surveys of households are necessary in order to understand travel behavior better so that models can be improved.

Data collection methods and frequency must be redesigned to better describe performance over time and over area. Use of municipalities as statistical units is questionable for assessing the balance between housing and jobs. A new generation of performance measures to replace LOS is also necessary.

High Density

Unless change in current low-density development patterns is encouraged, there is not much chance of getting change implemented. If sprawl is bad, it must be determined why. In order to be able to quantify the social costs that have remained unspecified in past studies, it is important to research and quantify all the costs and benefits of current development patterns, both low density and high density.

Dynamic Land Use Modeling

Planning tools are needed to forecast the impacts of transportation on development as well as on redevelopment.

Neotraditional Urban Design

High-priority research would include

- Evaluation of the benefits and disbenefits of such design.
- Development of techniques to use the principles of neotraditional design in a partially developed urban environment (retrofitting).

Congestion Pricing and Parking Pricing

Research priorities would include

- Methods to sell the concepts. Benefits and incentives for implementation must be clearly identifiable.
- Demonstration projects.
- An understanding of how the money obtained can be use to "double the impact" by providing feasible transportation alternatives to the user.

Research Management

An overarching priority is pulling together what has been learned in the past and will be learned in the future, synthesizing it, and codifying it in handbooks and manuals for ease of use. All future research should be tied to dissemination of the knowledge gained.

Replacement of the *ITE Manual*

A top priority should be the development of a manual or software that will assist in estimation of the impacts of alternative policies (e.g., parking management) on trip production at existing and new developments.

Maximally Efficient Suburban Activity Center

Previous research by Cervero (*9*), Schreffler (*10*), and others should be taken to the design stage. Design of new centers, as well as design of modifications to existing centers, should be included. Land use mix, density, development size, parking policies, and access by alternative modes should all be considered in developing designs that would increase transportation efficiency.

Behavioral Research

If efforts to convince people to behave in ways that are environmentally sensitive are to be successful, survey research and market research must be a high priority so that consumer preferences and reasons for consumer choices can be understood.

REFERENCES

1. Real Estate Research Corporation. *The Costs of Sprawl.* Council on Environmental Quality, Washington, D.C., 1974.
2. P. W. G. Newman and J. R. Kenworthy. *Cities and Automobile Dependence: A Sourcebook.* Gower, Brookfield, Vt., 1989.
3. J. Pucher. Urban Public Transport Subsidies in Western Europe and North America. *Transportation Quarterly,* Vol. 42, No. 3, July 1988, pp. 377–402.
4. J. Pucher. Urban Travel Behavior as the Outcome of Public Policy: The Example of Modal Split in Western Europe and North America. *Journal of the American Planning Association,* Vol. 54, No. 4, 1988, pp. 509–520.
5. Association for Commuter Transportation Parking Management Symposium, Seattle, Wash., December 6–7, 1990.
6. *Trip Generation Manual.* Institute of Transportation Engineers, 1976.
7. *Transportation Research Record 359,* TRB National Research Council, Washington, D.C., July 1990.
8. *Special Report 209: Highway Capacity Manual.* TRB, National Research Council, Washington, D.C., 1985.
9. R. Cervero. *America's Suburban Centers: A Study of the Land Use–Transportation Link.* Unwin Hyman, Boston, 1989.
10. E. Schreffler and M. D. Meyer. Evolving Institutional Arrangements for Employer Involvement in Transportation: The Case of Employer Associations. In *Transportation Research Record 914,* TRB, National Research Council, Washington, D.C. 1983, pp. 42–49.

Workshop 5

CHAIR: **Bruce D. McDowell**
SECRETARY: **Tai-Kuo Liu**
PARTICIPANTS: **David G. Burwell, Pete Fielding, Jane Howard, Jeffrey A. Parker, Peter L. Shaw, Frank Spielberg, Vergil G. Stover, W. T. Watterson, Debra Ann Whitmore**

Workshop 5 divided its task initially into two questions:

1. What knowledge is necessary in order to be able to plan and provide adequate transportation?
2. Within that, what is not known?

Answers to this second question produced a list of research needs that were then developed. Table 1 summarizes the workshop's findings and recommended directions for FHWA research. These findings and recommendations are explained in the following sections.

FINDINGS

With respect to the first question, the workshop participants identified 15 types of necessary information:

1. Environmental effects and imperatives
2. Modal relationships
    a. "Mobility" goals
    b. Intermodal (transfer penalties)
3. Time dimensions (short-range, long-range) and their speed of change
4. Intergovernmental roles
    a. Responsibilities
    b. Including public and private sectors

TABLE 1 SUMMARY OF WORKSHOP 5

Need to Know (Process Goals for Improving Transportation)	*Don't Know* (Research Needs)	*Methodology* (Research Direction and Products)	*Policy/Institutional* (Customers for the Research Results)
I. What drives transportation demand —an increasingly complex set of factors	Credible, iterative, interactive forecast of system performance —economic, environmental, behavioral	• New generation (Family) of models, Better data; tools for data development—addressing performance goals	• Interagency development • User friendly • Federal dissemination • Bigger data
II. Options for public action —Growth management —Urban design —Financial incentives —Etc.	• Their effects • How to apply them	• Evaluation studies • Operational studies	• Standard study process • Federal dissemination • Incentive grants
III. Responsive public decision making	• How to coordinate (mediate) diverse response • How to moderate splintering of responsibilities	• Evaluate "success" stories • Study how to apply "good practices"	• Federal dissemination to top policy office • Reconsider federal MPO requirements
IV. How to "market" (price) adequate transportation improvements	How to calculate "true" costs, benefits, and liabilities (costing out, pricing, and billing)	• New systems of accounts —How to do —How much will they cost? —Reporting/communicating processes (options)	• Interagency development —Government Accounting Standards Board —Joint Financial Management Improvement Program —GAO/CBO —Corps of Engineers • DOT dissemination to top policy office

5. Development dynamics (land use–transportation effects), transportation demands, and their communication

6. Human expectations (behaviors, life-styles) and potentials for change

7. Demographic needs
    a. Growth/no-growth
    b. Changing composition (market segments)
    c. Changing locations

8. Recognition of limits on how many public facilities can be delivered

9. (New) options for public action (loss of some options?) and their effects (what works)

10. Effectiveness of urban design options in reducing number and length of trips

11. True costs of transportation and the value of transportation (mobility, service, a factor in economic production)

12. Travel behavior data

13. Effects of no action

14. Public decision dynamics (actors; institutional capabilities)

15. Protection of existing rights-of-way

These types of information can be organized into the following four groups:

1. Forces that are driving transportation demand these days;

2. Options for public action;

3. How to get public decision makers to support "adequate" mobility; and

4. How to market "adequate" transportation systems (i.e., how to price them to sell).

A brief elaboration on each of these "needs to know" follows, along with what the workshop members think is not known about them.

First, the participants agreed with Deakin and others that transportation demand factors have gotten much more numerous and more complex in recent years. These factors include not just the usual land use and demographic factors of housing and jobs but also the changing composition of populations, multiplying market segments, rising human expectations, changing life-styles, altered travel behavior, relationships among different modes of transportation, resistance to intermodel transfers, environmental effects and imperatives (including compliance with clean air legislation), energy considerations, and temporal as well as locational shifts in demand.

What is not available is a series of reliable, credible, iterative, and interactive forecasts of transportation system performance based on this current complex set of demand factors and the expanding set of policy options now becoming available.

Second, the participants agreed with Brand that the options available for public action are becoming much more numerous. In particular, "growth management" options seem to offer new potentials for firmly linking land use decisions to public facility decisions. Furthermore, urban design options may be able to reduce the number and length of trips. Financial incentives for favored types of development or preservation, and means of preserving existing rights-of-way, also could be quite important. But some options—such as urban renewal and urban development action grants—have been lost, and it needs to be recognized that there are practical limits to the amount of public facilities that can be provided.

What is not known, very often, is precisely what effect the available policy options would have if applied, and sometimes even how they should be applied.

Third, present public decision making processes do not seem to be supporting adequate programs for mobility. Growing congestion and rising deferred maintenance liabilities are two indicators of this decision making deficiency. Other indicators include the languishing roles of the metropolitan planning organizations (MPOs), the absence of state involvement with land use in most states, and the lack of concern with urban development issues by most federal agencies other than the U.S. Department of Transportation.

What is not known is how to coordinate (or mediate) the diverse responsibilities of the many local, state, regional, and federal units of government whose individual actions have significant effects on land development and transportation system performance. Many incentives in the present system of government tend to splinter responsibilities rather than to coordinate them.

Finally, Schulz's plea for help in marketing adequate transportation systems struck a responsive cord in the group.

What is not known is how to price the system to sell. True costs are not calculated, nor are true benefits to various groups, the true value of transportation as an element of economic production, or the true liabilities of transportation systems as measured by deferred maintenance costs or pollution potentials. If these costs, benefits, and liabilities are not known, the right people cannot be billed for the proper amounts—and real needs will continue to go unmet. The group agreed with the statement made earlier at this conference that the American people are willing to pay a fair price for value received. It is time to find out how to calculate that price.

In summary, then, the identified research needs are for

- Better and more useful forecasts of transportation system performance, impacts, and relationships with urban development;
- Better information about the effectiveness and means of implementing policy options;
- Means of coordinating (or mediating) the actions of diverse governments affecting the transportation and land development system; and
- A credible means of pricing and marketing transportation system improvements.

RECOMMENDATIONS

Based on its findings, the workshop recommended five research priorities to FHWA to help improve the process by which urban transportation is provided. In rough priority order, they are

1. Evaluation and operational studies of the growing number of new options for public action, so that what works and how to do it will be known;
2. Better data, more data, and tools for developing these data, so that present transportation demands can be understood and the best use made of existing transportation forecasting models;
3. Evaluations of public decision making "success stories" and how they can be applied elsewhere to help raise the responsiveness of governments to transportation needs;
4. Studies to develop a new system of accounts that will allow calculation of the true costs, benefits, and liabilities of transportation improvements and the "billing" of appropriate parties for their fair shares of the costs of these improvements; and
5. A new generation (family) of transportation system performance models that will allow the understanding and forecasting of the relationships between transportation demand and capacity and how alter-

native transportation facilities and programs will help to serve mobility needs, economic needs, environmental needs, energy needs, and social needs.

The top priority went to studies of new policy options—such as growth management, congestion management plans, urban design, and financial incentives for changing transportation behavior—because action is an imperative but knowledge about the consequences of those actions and implemention of such programs is not available. Overall, 11 studies of this type were suggested:

1. Congestion management plans
2. Growth management processes
3. Right-of-way preservation
4. Urban design
   a. Types of road design
   b. Connectivity
5. Financial incentives
   a. Parking congestion fees (pricing)
   b. Air quality implementation plans
      (enforcement measures)
   c. Fiscal zoning
6. HOV
7. Mobility limitations
8. TMAs
9. Employee-based trip reduction
   (traffic mitigation ordinances)
10. Impact monitoring
11. Goods movement interconnections

The "rush to action" may make transportation problems worse—rather than better—or may waste scarce resources with little benefit. Limited time and money exist to devote to new initiatives, and the group wanted to make sure that the most beneficial ones would be pursued.

When the U.S. Department of Transportation identifies and "validates" the most promising of these new options—on the basis of credible research methods and reviews by "user panels"—it should disseminate that information vigorously and consider offering incentive grants to speed its use.

Better data, and tools for developing them more effectively and efficiently, earned the second priority, because the present transportation planning and evaluation processes are data starved. Current models cannot even be used, much less new, more data-intensive models. We need to learn to walk again with our present models, before we can run with new ones. Larger budgets are needed for this purpose.

Studies of the public decision making process are a high priority because most of the rest of what can be done comes to naught when proposals to meet transportation demands fall between the cracks in the intergovernmental system. Responsibilities for approving transportation improvements appear to be getting more numerous and more splintered every year, as more "market-based" special districts and toll road authorities come on-line. Coordination and mediation mechanisms appear to be receiving less attention in many urban areas than they did in the 1960s and 1970s. A reevaluation of the MPOs (and MPO requirements) is long overdue; new studies of new regional transportation authorities, unified transportation funds, and emerging regional air quality agencies are needed.

The fourth priority is development of a new system of accounts, because financing is becoming so crucial to providing adequate transportation facilities and services. Environmental, energy, and behavioral externalities are becoming greater concerns—and much more costly. Unfunded federal and state mandates are capturing more transportation dollars every year. System demands are outstripping available resources. Deferred maintenance, congestion, pollution, and energy waste are results.

But in the public sector, cost accounts, asset accounts, accrued liability accounts, and benefit accounts are not customarily kept. Transportation-related social costs and benefits, business costs and benefits, environmental costs and benefits, and the costs of delay cannot easily be identified and reported. Therefore, transportation services cannot be "priced" realistically, nor can the costs be assessed fairly among direct and indirect beneficiaries. Current trends are moving heavily toward the concept of payment by beneficiaries, so "pricing" is becoming increasingly important in the public sector.

The task of developing this new system of accounts will not be accomplished quickly or easily. Careful attention should be given to how such accounts can be established and maintained accurately and without excessive cost. Some members of the group feared that methodological and cost problems could make these accounts impractical. Others feared that explicit allocations of costs and benefits could be politically explosive. Still others felt that a key advantage of these accounts would arise from regular disclosure and discussion of the value of transportation, the costs of regulations, the accrual of deferred maintenance liabilities, and other key performance figures.

The study of new accounting systems should consider public reporting processes designed to enhance political and intergovernmental accountability. This study also should be conducted in cooperation with several other organizations interested in this issue—including the Governmental Accounting Standards Board, the Government Accounting Office, and the Congressional Budget Office—and should be aimed in large measure at top policy officials in all levels of government.

The recommendation for the development of a new generation of transportation and transportation-related models comes last because it is a complex, long-term, costly enterprise with uncertain results. For example, such models may require more data than most transportation agencies can afford, more interagency cooperation than can generally be achieved, and greater interdisciplinary integration than can be imagined. Integrated design and use of a compatible family of models are necessary; separate models cannot be left in separate agencies, unrelated to each other. These new models must be good for small-area analysis as well as for large-scale planning, they should be longitudinal, they must respond to environmental objectives as well as the needs of increasingly diverse segments of the transportation consumer market, they must accept many policy options as variables, and they must be "transparent" enough for policymakers to place confidence in them.

Despite the difficulties, such models are worth pursuing. Other federal agencies—especially the U.S. Environmental Protection Agency—should be involved conceptually and financially. A wide range of potential users also should be consulted, so that any new models will have the greatest possible usefulness. Cost sharing of development and data costs might improve the feasibility of this task.

If such models are developed, the U.S. Department of Transportation and other federal agencies should support a major training effort to ensure that they will be used widely and wisely.

The group believes that pursuit of these five high priorities for urban transportation research by the federal government has the potential to replace pessimism with optimism about being able to get on top of current transportation problems.

Steering Committee
Biographical Information

George T. Lathrop, *Chairman*, is Deputy Director of Transportation for the city of Charlotte, North Carolina. He has a bachelor's degree in civil engineering from North Carolina State University, a master's degree in city planning from Yale University, and a doctorate in planning from the University of North Carolina. He headed the Research Section of the New York Department of Transportation from 1962 to 1966 and served as lecturer at the University of North Carolina Department of City and Regional Planning from 1966 to 1973, as Associate at Kimley-Horn from 1973 to 1975, and as Vice President of John Hamburg and Associates from 1975 to 1982. He is a member of the American Institute of Certified Planners, the Institute of Transportation Engineers, and the American Society of Civil Engineers. He is past chairman of the TRB Committee on Transportation and Land Development and is currently chairman of the TRB Strategic Management Committee.

Paul E. Benson is a Research Engineer with the California Department of Transportation (Caltrans). He has a B.S. and an M.S. in civil engineering from the University of California, Davis. He has served in various capacities with Caltrans, and is currently Chief, Air Quality, Noise, Energy and Vibration Branch. He chairs the TRB Committee on Transportation and Air Quality and is a member of the ASCE Committee on Energy and Environmental Aspects of Transportation.

Dianne R. Brake is President of the Middlesex Somerset Mercer Regional Council (a nonpartisan private-sector planning and research organization in central New Jersey). She has a B.A. in sociology and Russian studies from Hollins College, an M.F.A. in planning and social design from the California Institute of the Arts, and has completed doctoral studies in sociology at the University of Edinburgh. She has worked as a researcher for the Royal Institute of British Architects and as a policy analyst for the Center for Health Facilities

189

Research, Trenton, New Jersey. She has been an adjunct faculty member of the Lincoln Institute of Land Policy and a trustee of the Greater Princeton Transportation Management Association.

David G. Burwell is cofounder and President of Rails-to-Trails Conservancy, a nonprofit membership organization providing advocacy, technical assistance, and legal and educational services to public and private institutions for the purpose of converting abandoned rail corridors to public trail use. He was an attorney with the National Wildlife Federation for 10 years before establishing Rails-to-Trails. He is a graduate of Dartmouth College and the University of Virginia Law School. He is a member of the TRB Transportation Law Section.

Elizabeth A. Deakin is Assistant Professor, Department of City and Regional Planning, University of California, Berkeley, and President of Deakin, Harvey, Skabardonis, Inc., a Berkeley-based consulting firm. She has an S.B. and S.M. in political science and civil engineering from Massachusetts Institute of Technology and a J.D. from Boston College. She currently chairs the TRB Committee on Transportation and Land Development.

G. Bruce Douglas III is a transportation planner in private practice who specializes in travel demand analysis and the impact of land use on travel demand estimates. He has a B.S. in civil engineering from Princeton and an M.S.C.E. and Ph.D. from the University of Pennsylvania. He worked as a Senior Project Manager for Peat, Marwick, Mitchell and as Program Manager for Louis Klauder and Associates before establishing his own firm, Douglas and Douglas, Inc., in 1981. He is a member of the TRB Committee on Transportation and Land Development.

Robert T. Dunphy is Director of Transportation Research for the Urban Land Institute. He has a B.S. in civil engineering from Catholic University and an M.S. in civil engineering from Texas A&M University. He was Assistant Director, Technical Services, with the Metropolitan Washington Council of Governments from 1972 to 1984 and Senior Associate at PRC Engineering from 1984 to 1985. He is a member of the TRB Committee on Transportation and Land Development and the Task Force on Transportation Demand Management.

Sheldon M. Edner is Chair of the Department of Public Administration at Portland State University. He has a B.A. in political science from Humboldt State University and an M.A. and Ph.D. in political science from the University of California, Riverside. He served as a lecturer at the University of California, Riverside; as Assistant Professor of American Government and Environmental Policy at Humboldt State University; as Assistant Professor, Political Science, at Eastern Michigan University; and as Professor of Urban Studies and Public Administration at Portland State University. He is a member of the American Society for Public Administration, the Urban Affairs Association, and the American Political Science Association, and is currently chair of the TRB Committee on Intergovernmental Relations and Policy Processes.

David L. Greene is a senior research staff member in the Center for Transportation Analysis at Oak Ridge National Laboratory. He has a B.A. from Columbia University, an M.A. from the University of Oregon, and a Ph.D. in geography and environmental engineering from Johns Hopkins University. He has been on the staff of the Oak Ridge National Laboratory since 1978 and is currently Leader of the Energy Policy Research Group. He is past chairman of the TRB Committee on Energy Conservation and Transportation Demand and currently chairs the TRB Energy and Environmental Concerns Section.

Gary Hawthorn is President of Gary Hawthorn Associates, Ltd., a transportation and environmental consulting firm. He has a B.S. in humanities and technology from Drexel University, an M.S. in civil engineering from Massachusetts Institute of Technology, an M.B.A. from Harvard University, and an M.S. in environmental science from Drexel University. He worked for the New Jersey Department of Environmental Protection from 1964 to 1970; OEC Din, Paris, France, from 1973 to 1974; and in various capacities for the Environmental Protection Agency from 1970 to 1990. He is a member of the TRB Task Force on Transportation Demand Management.

Bruce D. McDowell is Director, Government Policy Research, Advisory Commission on Intergovernmental Relations (ACIR). He has a B.A. in sociology from American University, an M.C.P. from Georgia Institute of Technology, and a Ph.D. in public administration from American University. He worked for the Maryland National Capital Park and Planning Commission from 1959 to 1963, ACIR from 1963 to 1964, and the Metropolitan Washington Council of Governments from 1964 to 1972. He returned to ACIR in 1972, where he has worked to the present time except during 1986–1988 when he was Director of Governmental Studies for the National Council on Public Works Improvement. He is a member of the American Institute of Certified Planners and is past chairman of the TRB Committee on Intergovernmental Relations and Policy Processes. He is currently chairman of the TRB Transportation Systems Planning Section.

Michael D. Meyer is Professor of Civil Engineering, Georgia Institute of Technology, and Director of the Georgia Tech Transportation Research and Education Center. He has a B.S. in civil engineering from the University of Wisconsin, an M.S. from Northwestern University, and a Ph.D. from Massachusetts Institute of Technology. He was Associate and Assistant Professor in the Department of Civil Engineering at MIT from 1978 to 1983 and Director of the Bureau of Transportation Planning and Development at the Massachusetts Department of Public Works from 1983 to 1988. He currently chairs the TRB Committee on Statewide Multimodal Transportation Planning and the Task Force on Transportation Demand Management.

H. Pike Oliver is Vice President and Manager, Southern California Planning and Processing, Southwest Diversified, Inc. He has a B.A. in urban studies from San Francisco State University and an M.A. in urban planning from the University of California, Los Angeles. He has worked for the Contra Costa County Planning Department, City of New York, the California State Department of Finance, California Office of Planning and Research, the Irvine Company, and Aries Properties. He is a member of the Urban Land Institute and the American Planning Association.

Richard H. Pratt is Principal, Richard H. Pratt, Consultant, Inc., specializing in transportation planning. He has a B.S. from the California Institute of Technology and an M.S. in civil engineering from Northwestern University. He was previously with Barton-Aschman Associates and Alan M. Voorhees and Associates, and is a member of the TRB Committee on Transportation and Land Development and the Project Panel for Quick Response Transferable Parameters.

Darwin G. Stuart is Manager, Planning and Research, Chicago Transit Authority. He has an M.S. in transportation science from Northwestern University, an M.A. in urban planning from the University of Illinois, Urbana-Champaign, and a Ph.D. in civil engineering from Northwestern

University. He was Principal Associate at Barton-Aschman Associates before his current position with CTA. He is a member of the American Planning Association and a member of the TRB Committees on Strategic Management, Transportation and Land Development, and Transportation Programming, Planning, and Systems Evaluation.

Martin Wachs is Professor of Urban Planning, School of Architecture and Urban Planning, University of California, Los Angeles. He has a B.S.C.E. from the City University of New York and an M.S. and Ph.D. from Northwestern University. He is the author of three books and many articles on urban transportation planning, public transportation fare and subsidy policy, transportation problems of the elderly, and the relationship among transportation, land use, and air quality.

W. T. Watterson is President of the Watterson West Group, Inc., in Seattle. Previously, he was Director of Technical Services at the Puget Sound Council of Governments, where he was responsible for the economic, demographic, and transportation data collection, analysis, and forecasting programs, as well as the agency computer systems. He has an M.R.P. from the University of North Carolina, and a Ph.D. in city and regional planning from the University of Pennsylvania. He is a member of several professional associations and of the TRB Committees on Transportation Planning Applications and Transportation and Land Development.

George V. Wickstrom is Manager, Technical Services, Metropolitan Washington Council of Governments. He has a B.S. in civil engineering from Cooper Union College and a graduate certificate in highway traffic from Yale University. He has worked for the Edwards and Kelcey Firm and also the Penn-Jersey Transportation Study, the New Castle County Land Use and Transportation Planning Program, and the Capital Regional Transportation Planning Board. He has been past chairman of various TRB committees.

Julian Wolpert is Henry G. Bryant Professor of Geography, Public Affairs and Urban Planning, Woodrow Wilson School of Public International Affairs, Princeton University. He has an A.B. in economics and geography from Columbia University and an M.S. and Ph.D. in geography from the University of Wisconsin. He was previously a faculty member of the Regional Science Department at the University of Pennsylvania. He is a member of the National Academy of Sciences and also a member of the TRB Executive Committee.

Participants

Bartholomew, Keith, 1000 Friends of Oregon, 534 Southwest 3rd Avenue, Suite 300, Portland, OR 97204

Bay, Paul N., BRW, Inc., 700 Third Street South, Minneapolis, MN 55415

Belanger, Trina T., Maricopa Association of Governments, 1820 W. Washington, Phoenix, AZ 85007

Benson, Daniel, E., Daniel Benson & Associates, 2555 E. Chapman Avenue, Suite 600, Fullerton, CA 92631

Borchert, John R., University of Minnesota, 267-19th Avenue South, Minneapolis, MN 55455

Brand, Daniel, Charles River Associates, Inc., 200 Clarendon Street, 43rd Floor, Boston, MA 02116

Burwell, David G., President, Rails-to-Trails Conservancy, 1400 16th Street, NW, Suite 300, Washington, DC 20036

Coleman, Thomas G., EG&G Dynatrend, Inc., Kendall Square, Cambridge, MA 02142

DeCorla-Souza, Patrick T., Federal Highway Administration, 400 Seventh St., SW, HPN-22, Washington, DC 20590

Deakin, Elizabeth A., University of California, Berkeley, Department of County and Regional Planning, 228 Wurster Hall, Berkeley, CA 94720

Douglas, G. Bruce III, Douglas & Douglas, Inc., 4400 East-West Highway, Suite 1026, Bethesda, MD 20814

Ducca, Frederick W., Federal Highway Administration, 400 7th Street, SW, HPN-22, Washington, DC 20590

Dunphy, Robert T., The Urban Land Institute, 625 Indiana Avenue, NW, Suite 400, Washington, DC 20004

Dyett, Michael V., Blayney Dyett Greenberg, 70 Zoe Street, #100, San Francisco, CA 94107

Edner, Sheldon M., Portland State University, P.O. Box 751, Portland, OR 97207

Emerson, Donald J., Urban Mass Transportation Administration, 400 7th Street, SW, Washington, DC 20590

Fielding, Pete, Institute for Transportation Studies, University of California, Irvine, Irvine, CA 92717

Fitzpatrick, Hugh, The Irvine Company, 550 Newport Center Drive, 6th Floor, Newport Beach, CA 92660

Fleet, Christopher R., Federal Highway Administration, 400 7th Street, SW, HEP-22, Washington, DC 20590

Gerwig, Kathy L., Senior Vice President, The Breen Consortium, PO Box 191486, San Francisco, CA 94119

Glasgow, Norman M., Jr., Wilkes, Artis, Hedrick & Lane, 1666 K Street, NW, Suite 1100, Washington, DC 20006

Glaze, Richard S., Harland Bartholomew & Associates, Inc., 2701 Union Avenue Extended, Memphis, TN 38112

Gordon, Deborah, Union of Concerned Scientists, 1616 P Street, N.W., Washington, D.C. 20590

Guiliano, Genevieve, University of Southern California, School of Urban & Regional Planning, Los Angeles, CA 90089

Hamburg, John R., Barton-Aschman Associates, Inc, 1133 15th Street, NW, Suite 901, Washington, DC 20005

Hawthorn, Gary, Gary Hawthorn Associates Ltd., P.O. Box 1160, Fort Myer Station, VA 22211

Horn, Richard J., Research and Special Programs Administration, U.S. Department of Transportation, Kendall Square, Cambridge, MA 02142

Howard, Jane, Howard/Stein-Hudson Associates, 38 Chauncy Street, Boston, MA 02111

Joseph, Robert, California Department of Transportation, District 12, 2501 Pullman Street, Santa Ana, CA 92705

Judd, Lynne B., Wisconsin Department of Transportation, P.O. Box 7913, Madison, WI 53707-7913

Juhasz, Barna, Federal Highway Administration, 400 7th Street, SW, HEP-20, Washington, DC 20590

Kuhn, Veronica, Natural Resources Defense Council, 617 S. Olive Street, Los Angeles, CA 90014

Lathrop, George T., Deputy Director, City of Charlotte Department of Transportation, 600 East Fourth Street, Charlotte, NC 28202-2858

Lave, Charles, University of California, Irvine, Economics Department, Irvine, CA 92717

Lessieu, Eugene J., Port Authority of New York & New Jersey, One World Trade Center, 54E, New York, NY 10048

Liu, Tai-Kuo, Research and Special Programs Administration, U.S. Department of Transportation, Kendall Square, Cambridge, MA 02142

McCue, Patrick J., Florida Department of Transportation, 605 Suwannee Street, M.S. 57, Tallahassee, FL 32399-0450

McDowell, Bruce D., Advisory Commission on Intergovernmental Relations, Vanguard Building, #2000, 1111 20th Street, NW, Washington, DC 20575

Ogden, Kenneth W., University of California, Department of Civil Engineering, Irvine, CA 92717

Oliver, H. Pike, Southwest Diversified Co., Inc., 19200 Von Karman Avenue, Suite 400, Irvine, CA 92715

Parker, Jeffrey A., Jeffrey A. Parker & Associates, 5224 42nd Street, NW, Washington, DC 20015

Parning, Cynthia, Los Angeles County Transportation Commission, 403 W. 8th Street, Suite 500, Los Angeles, CA 90014

Pisarski, Alan E., Consultant, 6501 Waterway Drive, Falls Church, VA 22044

Porter, Douglas, Consultant, 5406 Trent St., Chevy Chase, MD 20815

Pratt, Richard H., Richard H. Pratt, Consultant, Inc., P.O. Box 158, Garrett Park, MD 20896-0158

Putman, Stephen H., University of Pennsylvania, Urban Simulation Laboratory, G-3 Meyerson Hall, Philadelphia, PA 19104

Reichert, James P., Orange County Transit District, 11222 Acacia Parkway, Garden Grove, CA 92642

Schneider, Jerry B., University of Washington, Department of Civil Engineering (FX-10), Seattle, WA 98195

Schulz, David F., Milwaukee County Executive, 901 N. 9th Street, Milwaukee, WI 53233

Seskin, Sam, Cambridge Systematics, 3373 Rittenhouse St., NW, Washington, DC 20015

Shaw, Peter L., California State University, Long Beach, Graduate Center for Public Policy, Long Beach, CA 90840

Skillette, Jerry, Central Parking Systems, 11500 Olympia Blvd, Suite 420, Los Angeles, CA 90064

Spielberg, Franklin L., SG Associates, Inc., 4200 Daniels Avenue, Annandale, VA 22003

Stover, Vergil G., Texas A&M University, College Station, TX 77843

Tustian, Richard, Lincoln Institute of Land Policy, 26 Trowbridge Street, Cambridge, MA 02138

Wachs, Martin, Graduate School of Architecture and Urban Planning, Perloff Hall, University of California, Los Angeles, CA 90024-1467

Waite, Wayne W., Urban Mass Transportation Administration, 400 7th Street, SW, UGM-20, Washington, DC 20590

Watterson, W.T., Puget Sound Council of Governments, 216 First Avenue South, Seattle, WA 98104

Weiner, Edward, Office of the Secretary, U.S. Dept of Transportation, 400 7th St SW, Rm 5102A, S-5, Washington, DC 20590

Whitmore, Debra Ann, Southern California Association of Governments, 818 W. Seventh Street, Los Angeles, CA 90012

Wickstrom, George V., Metropolitan Washington Council of Governments, 777 N. Capitol Street, NE, Washington, DC 20002-4239

Wilshusen, Linda J., Regional Transportation Commission, 701 Ocean Street, Room 406B, Santa Cruz, CA 95062